DYING
101:

A CANDID CONVERSATION
ON TERMINAL ILLNESS

The Updated Bestselling Guide

GAIL CASON-REISER, MICHAEL J. DEMORATZ, RICHARD J. REISER

DYING 101:
A CANDID CONVERSATION ON TERMINAL ILLNESS

By Gail Cason-Reiser, Michael J. Demoratz, Richard J. Reiser

Cover design, format, and chair illustration by Paul Gyuro

Printed in the United States of America

Library of Congress
Cataloging-in-Publications
96-92022

ISBN 9780964993815

Although this book may be titled DYING 101:,
It's really about living and how you choose to live the
time that you have left.

It's important to have these options explained to
you so that you can use whatever time is remaining
to be honest, to be open, to be direct, to be candid,
and to deal with your life as you choose.

What they are saying about this update

Dying 101: is a tool that will help individuals and society transform the dying process. You are giving detailed explanations of the truths and exposing the shallowness of so many myths. Most importantly, you are empowering individuals so that they become a partner in our sacred obligation to teach and love.

_____Mona El-Kurd, LSCW

Enjoyed and appreciated the approach these talented authors took. There are few people more qualified to prepare this book...While it was written for individuals to take ownership of the process and 'take an active role in controlling your life', I also found it to be useful in stimulating thoughts and different approaches to how I am dealing with my adult siblings in caring for our aging parents... I highly recommend the read for anyone whose parents are nearing their golden years and those who understand that planning for your personal end-of-life arrangements and decisions is as important as any other plan you will ever prepare.

_____Josh Luke, PhD

I think the tone is just right. It's inviting and draws people in to what can be a scary and off-putting issue. The book reads like a conversation between well-informed friends –like listening in on conversation at the next table over. A very accessible way to bring people into the topic. It will serve the purpose of empowering patients to ask better questions. The "Hidden Agenda" information was great. Something I haven't seen explained this clearly before.

_____Matthew Janssen, MD

Even after 40 years of doing this work, I found *Dying 101*: to be an incredibly powerful, moving and informative text. It was long on content and substance. The authors are practical and spiritual guides for this most sacred of all journeys. They dared to speak the unspeakable.

_____Stuart Bloom, PhD

Dying 101: makes an often-avoided topic accessible; it's an important entrée into the subject of dying. The no-punches-pulled dialogue shows people how they can 'own' the process and take actions to have it go as much as possible the way they want it to go. It's one thing to indulge in intellectual 'fun' thinking and talking about death, even one's own. It's quite another to be immersed in what in some respect amounts to a 'to-do' list for when it's really happening. It takes Kubler-Ross and expands beyond her observations to include a virtual constellation of people who are affected and how each of them may choose to be in those circumstances --- something of a script/rehearsal notes for what everyone will face. For that reason alone, it's a marvelous gift.

_____Donald Miller, Esq.

What they were saying about the original

Don't be turned off by the title. This book is super. I laughed and cried over many pages... This book is not just for the terminally ill; it is for family, friends, grandchildren, and business associates... This book should be in every house, library, doctor' office and human resources' office.

_____Herb Cohen, columnist for seniors

This is truly a valuable tool for everyone who will encounter death and loss in their lives.

_____American Home Health Hospice Newsletter

Even though we deal constantly with books on dying, death and grieving, it still seems strange to me to tell you that this book, Dying 101, is delightful. This book fills a gap. It tells you just about everything you need to know once you realize you probably aren't going to get well. It does it with humor, reality and, most importantly, hope.

_____Bereavement Magazine, Joy Johnson, reviewer

I've got to say it sure is powerful...remembering all our friends who have gone through so much. It's pretty hard to correct something that doesn't lack a thing.

_____Doug Fountain, Group Member

This book should be required reading, by patients as well as caregivers, as a guide to avoid some of the errors made by us already involved.

_____Jesselyn Dole, Mother

Acknowledgments

As with any work based so much on a gathering of personal experiences, this one owes a great obligation to many people, not only for what we learned on the subject of death and dying, but for the personal enrichment and growth that we have been so graciously and lovingly given.

And a special thanks to our reviewers and inspirers.
Judy Anselmo, RN
Stuart Bloom, PhD
Angie Dickson, RN
Mona El-Kurd, LCSW
Doug Fountain
Val Gold-Neil, PsyD
Paul Gyuro, BFA
Mathew Janssen, MD
Nicholas Jauregui, MD
Ron Kurtz, PhD
Josh Luke, MD
Donald Miller, JD
Patty Mouton, BA
Vincent Nguyen, DO
Henry Totzke, MA

A special thanks to Elizabeth Kubler-Ross, M.D., the mother of all who do this work. Her leadership can never be replaced.

Authors' Note

The personal experiences and histories shared here are composites offered to exemplify the multitudes of stories and issues we have encountered over the years. Sadly, while individuals themselves are different, the stories repeat themselves over and over. This book is sold with the understanding that the publisher and the authors are not engaged in rendering legal, medical or other professional services. If legal or other expert assistance is required, the services of a competent professional should be sought. The purpose of this book is to educate. The authors and publisher shall have neither liability nor responsibility to any person or entity with respect to any loss or damage caused, or alleged to be caused, directly or indirectly by the information contained in this book.

Contents

Introduction : Why We Did It

Richard: We have waited over 20 years before bringing you this 2nd edition of Dying 101. Much has happened and little has happened. While important issues such as health insurance, palliative care, and assisted suicide have been in the news and caused serious upheaval, most other issues have met with little change but with increasing awareness and interest. We are briefly introducing a significant alternative which we call Option 3, Assisted Slumber, for the end-of-life patient.

We've been asked repeatedly to respond to these changes and to update Dying 101. We were pleased to be asked to keep the same format and that comforting little easy chair to meet the needs of those experiencing waves of emotion.

For us, personally, one big difference is that we are much older and further into the last quarter of our lives. Old age has truly come into our awareness as part of the dying process -- a new and different perspective often shockingly real and large enough for another book.

As before, we are delivering these messages as part of our need to fulfill a sacred obligation. The messages were received by us over the years as facilitators and counselors for therapy/support groups and individuals with terminal illnesses and aging, their significant others, family, and friends. We try our best to faithfully represent the experiences, thoughts, and feelings of the scores of people with whom we have been privileged to share intense and remarkable time.

Most important to that sharing was an unfathomable depth of honesty and authenticity. In today's jargon, "transparency" was critical because so much on this subject is generally hidden from most of us.

One may read extensively about existential issues and have perhaps a small intellectual clue about life and death, but you'd learn almost nothing about the process of dying. We have had a choir of mentors who have taught us their truths and shared their minds, hearts, and spirits in the most intimate of relationships as we walked with them down the path which leads to "leaving the Planet." They paid an enormous price for what they had learned; they shared it with us as a magnificent gift. This book, like the 1st edition, is about passing along that gift in the hope that others will be able to fully live the whole of their lives without having to needlessly pay the high cost others have already paid.

"Dying" and "death" are words our society has taught us to run and hide from -- in the insane, ostrich like belief that we can escape them; that they are avoidable if we just pretend they're not there; that death isn't part of the life cycle. Well, we have spent years watching the results of that dishonesty and the suffering that could otherwise have been avoided -- psychologically, emotionally, and physically.

You will find that we have tried to be faithful to the message of honesty and to be "righteous" in how and what we say. We know there are those who may be offended by the 101 Group and the desire of its members to honor their truth because there is no time to sugar-coat it nor for time-wasting niceties. B.S. by any other name still has all the properties of B.S. and worrying about language when you are dying is a real waste of precious energy. The personal experiences and histories shared here are composites offered to exemplify the multitudes of stories and issues we have encountered over the years. Sadly, while individuals themselves are different, the stories repeat themselves over and over.

For Gail and me, this is particularly personal. She first contacted a terminal illness over 40 years ago, surviving long enough to have been cleared this year by a "miracle" drug. I spent the better part of a year in chemotherapy for cancer. We are well-experienced patients and caregivers -- if only with each other. Yes, it's personal.

The conversational format herein was chosen to help us stay away from the artificiality inherent in sentences such as the ones you are now reading. We did limit the dialog to only two speakers (Gail and Michael) to keep things from getting confusing, even though the contents are a combination of all three of us and don't necessarily reflect the thoughts or experiences of the speaker indicated.

We wanted this to be easily read and used by people who may not always be feeling well and strong. So, we insisted that the type be big, the lines short, and the margins wide for notes and thoughts.

We know that all of us, ill, injured, or just aged, are treading the same path to the same inevitable conclusion; some of us are just further along than others. We hope we can help smooth out the bumps and cracks in that path for all of us.

Before you go any further, we are obligated to let you know that much of what is said here can be very difficult to hear, to assimilate, and to act on. It may be frightening, and it may be painful. It is our deepest belief that, with knowledge, the fear and pain you've probably been carrying around with you can be met head on. And, that empowered with knowledge and truth, you can learn to gain more control over your life and your responses to what's happening to and for you.

In the meantime, what you hear on these pages may be difficult. So, please take your time and take care of yourself. If things get too heavy, just put the book down and take a break. You'll find a little easy chair on the page at various points. These are places we've anticipated might be a spot to put down the book, sit back, take some relaxing deep breaths, and make some time for yourself and your thoughts. It's part of your taking control.

Having said that, we welcome you to the 101 Group. A group of people like yourself with some things they'd like to share -- love, courage, and knowledge.

Gail: Thanks, Richard. See you later. Shall we begin? Michael, let's start by welcoming our new group members and going over some guidelines.

Michael: Yes. Don't interrupt. One person talks at a time. Don't tell another group member that he or she is wrong. Everyone has the right, the obligation even, to speak his or her own truth. If you're tired or upset, please say "goodnight" before you leave so we don't think you're wandering the halls. We honor your need to leave, but we encourage you to stay until the end.

Gail: I think that's enough for now. Let's begin. To join in, you've got the margins on each page for your own comments, thoughts, questions, and lists.

Message 1: The Itinerary

Making Plans - You're Not Dead Yet

Gail: When going on a long vacation, you usually make a list of things you need to take care of prior to leaving. Before leaving, you arrange for the care of your children or small animals, watering the plants, taking care of the paper, the mail, etc. In the same way, you want to look at the medical, financial, legal, and personal arrangements that you need to make. You see, there should also be an itinerary for dying, just as you would for any long trip.

Getting "The News"

Michael: Your trip usually begins when you get the "The News." You, Richard, and I recently saw a powerful stage play about a woman and her dying and death experience with cancer. In the first scene, a woman was in her doctor's office. He threw "The News" at her, "You have some sort of cancer." She immediately ran to her head, trying to figure out what having cancer really meant, rather than listening to the physician who was continuing to talk. We have discussed how information like that comes at you in waves. You may see the crest of the wave but nothing that comes after that.

Gail: Yes, what we've been told is that it's like being paralyzed, like going catatonic. Everything shuts down externally, and you immediately retreat internally.

Michael: And that is exactly what happened to the woman in the play. She went inside and stopped listening to anything that was said after that point. There's a lot of information coming at you, and you're not paying attention, much less absorbing or hearing it.

Gail: Initial reactions can be deceiving. Generally speaking, the more intelligent you are, the more experienced you are in dealing with people, then the cleverer you will be at disguising the trauma.

Michael: Others may see facial expressions and

mannerisms that say, "Yes, I'm listening to you." But inside they'd hear screaming, "Let me out of here! Let me run away -- as far away from this as possible!"

Gail: So, you shut down. In some cases, you don't move. You don't breathe. And quite often some doctors, in an attempt to get "The News" out to you as rapidly as possible, don't allow you the necessary time to collect your thoughts. Like the doctor in the play, they continue to talk. The only problem is that you're not hearing them. It's unpleasant for them, so they move quickly through the information, and you are left with the lasting effects of the encounter.

Michael: There are two opposite extremes that don't help in these situations. One extreme is created by the physician who just drops the bomb and then walks out of the room. Intentionally walks out of the room! They give "The News" and say, "I want you to think about that" -- and they're off, anticipating that the patient will ask few, if any questions! And all you hear is just "The News," and then you go into shock or trauma or free-floating anxiety. The other extreme is created by the physician who wants to give tons of information -- too much information for you to process at one time -- and you go into overload and don't hear any of lt.

Gail: We know this happens. We've heard it enough times from people who've faced these problems.

Michael: Yes, we have.

Gail: We can't really advise you at this point because you've probably already had this experience. You've come here to get information from this point forward. So, basically, we're simply acknowledging your experience.

Michael: And we're also validating that it was not fun.

Gail: It wasn't fun, and it wasn't an isolated event. You're not alone. Everyone experiences the same thing. Regardless of their age. Regardless of the diagnosis. Regardless of the information. Sometimes people tend to "catastrophize" things. And, if they hear words like cancer, congestive heart failure or CHF, Alzheimer's, pulmonary disease --

whatever -- they are automatically catapulted in their minds to their own death because of things that they've seen or heard over the years.

Michael: It's a paralyzing event. I have often worked with people who have received "The News" 7 or 8 years ago, and they're still traumatized and paralyzed. They usually begin talking to me about things as if they had just gotten "The News" at that moment!

Gail: What about the personality who is a doer? A problem-solver? Those who will take the news and instantly go into action, making decisions prematurely based on limited information and limited experience. In jumping to the end, in seeing their death, in seeing the final outcome, they have omitted the year, the 5 years, the 10 years or more -- whatever period of time they have left.

Michael: You're talking about those who have just received some bad information, and they've started to make plans way before they need to. For example, someone who turns over all their money and all their possessions to a significant other so that if they died today their assets could be disposed of immediately. And then they don't die.

Gail: Exactly! And I was looking at it a little more personally. I'm someone who has experienced major catastrophic events. I have been given the news, and it's as if I'm being held down and I need to move. My personality is such that I immediately go into action. Action for me means I become super woman. I clean the house; I clean the garage; I get all the filing done; I clean up all my affairs. I'm in motion from the moment I hear the bad news until I'm physically and emotionally exhausted. Then I collapse somewhere. For me, it's a kind of running that occurs. We've seen it in group. We've seen clients come in -- generally at the burn out phase of that experience. They will run and run, or they will hide -- carrying some event to the extreme. When they're exhausted -- when they're physically, mentally and spiritually exhausted – that's often when they come into group and ask for assistance.

Michael: I've seen you in your almost manic routine. I know that others see it as heroic when, in fact, you're burning off fear energy.

Gail: Yes. This can be misleading and confusing for the observer and the patient.

Michael: If you are the patient, and are hearing or reading all this, you may find this a good opportunity to think back over what occurred for you within the first few days, weeks, and months after you got "The News." What did you do? Did you do anything that you wish you hadn't or anything that you might want to change? You might consider going back and cleaning up, straightening out, or making amends.

Gail: Going back now and cleaning up is very appropriate and can be an important, even critical, reliever of stress.

Michael: And if you're reading this, we've got to stand up and applaud you because you are already taking actions in a very positive way.

Different Ways to Take Your Trip

Gail: From the beginning, there are going to be options to select from in planning your itinerary, and you will probably need to ask questions to find out what those options are. It will always be a matter of how much you want to plan and control your own trip. Your role in directing your medical care will be a function of how strongly you want to address your disease. This may often change along the way from aggressive care to comfort measures alone. Aggressive treatment can be chemotherapy, radiation, experimental protocols, oral medication, or possibly some form of prolonged IV Infusion. Most forms of what is called "life support" are considered to be aggressive treatment. Some major things that are used for life support include IV's and feeding tubes, breathing tubes, or ventilators. Certain types of drugs. For instance, certain types of medication that will prolong heart function.

Michael: Right. We don't want to make you all junior physicians, but it is important for you to understand that you can learn some of the language that will be used and begin to read between the lines so you can ask the right questions.

Gail: And we know that it takes a lot of courage for you to ask questions because you have to be prepared to hear the answer.

Michael: One of the things about medical care that is important for you to understand is that on one side of the fence is "aggressive treatment" and on the other side is "palliative care."

Gail: What is meant by "palliative care"?

Michael: "Palliative care" is attending to the symptoms of the disease without curing the disease. Addressing such things as pain, nausea, vomiting, diarrhea, constipation, headaches, skin problems. The things that are going to make you uncomfortable. This is a specialty that can be used if necessary for years prior to hospice or end-of-life care.

Gail: That would include monitoring for bedsores, making sure you're clean and that you don't smell, so that you are acceptable to yourself and to others. Keeping you out of pain.

Michael: Proper nutrition is another aspect of palliative care. A palliative focus would be that you should be able to eat what you want without restrictions. Palliative care can be a feeding tube.

Gail: And chemotherapy, radiation, or experimental drugs.

Michael: Right. Although, in some instances, palliative care will include radiation or chemotherapy to shrink tumor size -- for comfort primarily. And that's something that really has to be spelled out. The physician really needs to be honest with you. "What we're doing is not curing you. What we're doing is making you more comfortable." For the long-term patient, ALS, CHF, Alzheimer's, and others, palliative care could be in place for years.

Gail: One of the more important areas to consider with palliative care has to do with surgery. Because quite often when you are in an advanced state of disease, any kind of surgical procedure can become a wound that does not heal.

Michael: You need to know why a surgical procedure is being performed. What is its purpose? Am I strong enough to heal?

What is the reasonably expected outcome? Will it heal?

Gail: In "A's" situation, for example, she was being treated with chemo and radiation therapy for cancer on her foot. The treatment was successful in that it raised the cancer to the surface of the foot. But it did so in such an aggressive manner that it created blisters and a very ugly sore. Some physician made the decision at that point to exfoliate the foot, meaning cut away the dead area. Now this led to her having a quarter of her foot with an open wound, draining constantly. It stunk to high heaven. And there was no way that this foot was going to heal. Finally, at the end-stage of her disease, the physician said to her in an off-the-cuff manner, "By the way, that sore on your foot is never going to close." She eventually died of septicemia, massive infection. It was a horrible problem for her for the last 2 to 3 months of her life.

Where Are You?

Michael: You need to ask yourself some questions. What is your body telling you through the symptoms that are coming up? If you're not able to eat, if you're no longer hungry, or if you need to have a feeding tube, what do those things mean? If having a feeding tube is going to give you longer life, what will be the quality of that life?

Gail: You're going to lose weight if you've been very ill for a long time and not consuming enough calories. You're not eating enough because your body is saying, "I'm not hungry. I don't need all this food. I'm shutting down."

Michael: And you have to come to that conclusion yourself. You have to be very clear about the message your body is giving you. If your body is saying. "Hey, I'm not ready to leave the Planet yet. I need more food, and I can't get enough in because I've got this swallowing problem." Then, perhaps going on the feeding tube is a wise choice. However, you can say no. Remember that getting the necessary calories to maintain your body weight can increase fluid volume in your body, which can depress your respiratory system -- because the fluid is going to need to go somewhere.

Gail: So, if your digestive tract is closing down, a natural part of the dying process, then the fluids are going to create other problems.

Michael: Putting you on a liquid, tube-fed nutrition allows for quite a volume of material to enter, and if your kidneys are not working properly, your heart is going to work hard pushing around fluid.

Gail: If they're giving you the calorie count of a normal, healthy adult for your age and body weight and you're not able to exercise, then those calories are going to turn into nothing but fat. So, there's something else that you need to look at. If the prognosis is good for recovery, then by all means any temporary nutritional infusion may be justified, but not if the rest of your body is deteriorating to the point where you will never regain muscle mass, good motor coordination, and quality of life.

Michael: And the only way that you can get that is by being honest with yourself, being honest with your physician, being honest with your family about what you want. They can keep you alive for a long time, but the quality of your life is going to change. I've noticed a fascinating thing about people who are nearing their death and finally admit that they are dying; they perked up after they stopped the IV's that forced fluids into their veins. Their level of alertness improved; they felt stronger; they felt more capable of participating in life. That's the most important thing when we talk about quality of life -- are you participating? Are you participating in the day-to-day activities of your life -- even if they have shrunk down to doing just some minor things? Such things as reading the newspaper, or reading part of the newspaper, or playing with the dog for a little bit, or your cat, or some other minor but valuable activity. Are you participating in life? If you're just existing, is that what you want?

Gail: You mentioned hospice. Because of the confusion many people have about this, perhaps this is a good place to talk a little about it. First. what is it, and where is it?

Michael: Most people still think of hospice as a place where you go to die. In truth, hospice is not a place but a philosophy of care during your final days in which the focus is on pain management and comfort. Not cure. Hospice is not a place - it can be a special facility which specializes in this care, but it doesn't have to be. It is a type of care provided wherever you are, regardless of the setting, be it at home, hospital, or nursing facility.

Gail: When hospice is provided at home, how is it different from home health care?

Michael: I think this is where many people do get confused. While hospice programs do vary, the key components of any Medicare-certified hospice program are the services provided by a treatment team consisting of a physician, a nurse, a social worker, a home health aide, chaplains, and volunteers, I refer to the Medicare hospice benefit because so many insurance companies base their hospice benefit on Medicare's. If you don't yet qualify for Medicare, you should check with your insurance provider to see exactly what they will do.

Gail: How else is hospice different?

Michael: Let's see. You and your family must be provided with whatever services are needed to keep you comfortable, including medication for pain and whatever medical equipment or any hardware that is necessary to assist in your health care management. If you are at home, it is brought in for you.

Gail: What about costs?

Michael: Hospice care is provided by Medicare, Medicaid and private insurance, generally with little or no deductibles or coinsurance. It is important for you to ask if any deductibles are required by you before you sign on to a service.

Gail: O.K., but home health has nurses and social workers and aides, too. Why would one choose hospice over home health if you are still at home?

Michael: I think it's important to state here that if you are terminally ill, no longer treating your condition aggressively, and are looking for a comfort-centered approach, then hospice is the direction to go. The people involved are experts at addressing care needs at the end of life. Additionally, they are available to your family, partner and close ties for support now and later on after you've died.

Gail: Obviously, hospice is not for everyone unless they meet the admission criteria and desire this approach.

Michael: Absolutely. Hospice should not in any way be forced. But it should be offered to those who could benefit from it. It is an important option for those that want it.

Gail: This takes me back to our discussion about being aware. Accepting what's happening to your body; taking that on in a loving way -- not in a shaming way. Really trying to comprehend what it is that's going on and what your needs are. You will need a clear understanding of the term "hospice." Hospice focuses on your comfort to better the quality of your life.

Michael: Where do you think the patient would be during "hospice," a skilled nursing facility, residential board and care, or at home?

Gail: Hospice can go on at home or in some kind of skilled nursing facility. I use the term "facility" because I want you to be clear that it's not necessarily "hospice". You can go into a skilled nursing facility very early on and stay there for months or even years, or you can go in for a short period of time and then be released.

Michael: Exactly.

Gail: That's an option for you if you are alone or you do not have adequate family support around you. It doesn't have to mean that you are near death; some patients who are "late-stage" are confused about that. They assume that unless they can go home, they're about to die. So, if the discharge planner comes in and says, "We want to put you in a skilled facility," the patient fights it rather than saying, "Oh, okay. What is the program going to be? Am I going to be able to go into this skilled facility and then out for a period of time? Or are you, in fact telling me that I'm dying and that I'm going to die in this facility?" What we're trying to do is give you the language so that it is very clear for you and your healthcare providers.

Michael: That's an excellent point. You need to ask the question, "Are you telling me I need to go into the skilled nursing facility because I need care in order to get better so that I can return to my living environment at home, or are you telling me that I'm dying?"

Gail: Exactly!

Michael: And that's a difficult question to ask!

Gail: It is only difficult if you are afraid of the answer. Or if the key person you ask the question of will turn away, or give you a lie, or pat you on the hand and tell you not to worry. In other words, there's some built-in fear -- not around your hearing the answer but around
their reaction to your questions.

Michael: It is a typical example of what leads to a conspiracy of silence.

Gail: So, be direct: "Are you telling me that I'm dying?"

Michael: And that is probably the best question for you, the patient, to ask - hoping that you can get a direct response from the doctor or whoever is working with you. They could respond with something like, "Well, I think we're just going to tune you up for a little bit and see where things go." You might then want to ask, "What does that mean?" What you want to do is pin the doctor down. You want to maintain an intimate sense of involvement in what's happening to your body.

Gail: "W", for example, was a man who was not in touch with his body. So, when his physician came in and said, "Okay, "W", we need to discharge you now," "W" was not able to look down and say, "Oh, my G-d, I can't walk, I can't get myself to the toilet! I can't get myself in and out of the shower, I can't even go into the kitchen and prepare a light meal! How can I go home?"

Michael: This is an example of the need to do a "systems check", "Hey, what's going on in this body? I need to have someone prepare my meals. I need to have diapers because I can't control my bowels. I need to have someone lift me out of bed and put me in a wheelchair or on the toilet. I need some one in my home to care for me."

Gail: There are other questions that you need to ask on discharge, such as, "Am I now going to be able to walk alone?" One of the easiest ways for you to confirm your status is to find out from the nurse or aide. When they come in, ask them to walk with you to the bathroom. If, in fact, the nurse or the aide refuses to do that, guess what?

You're probably not going to be able to do that at home. If you have trouble feeding yourself, for whatever reason, opening up the little cartons of food that the aide has brought in, cutting up your meat, or opening up the little paper that the straw is in, or just sitting there and putting the food in your mouth, guess what? You're probably not going to be able to get up and walk to the kitchen and make yourself a sandwich! There are some things that you can be aware of -- questions you can ask yourself to help get in touch with your present physical condition. Are they moving me? Are they walking me? Are they exercising me? Are they preparing me to go home?" And if you can't honestly answer these questions, then find out from your physician what kind of care or help you need, and where would be the best place to get that help.

Michael: Pay attention to the fact that what's happening to you in the hospital may be the result of a deterioration in your health. "Oh, gosh, I do need to have someone help me do those things. And perhaps I'm going to need someone to cook for me and clean for me." Sometimes we take that for granted. I remember talking with a patient who thought, "Oh, my mother will do all that," as if it would all just miraculously happen at home.

After hearing he had been in a skilled nursing facility for quite some time, I said to him, "You don't know all of the people that are involved in your care at this point!" I said, "You have a housekeeper that comes in and cleans your room several times a day. You have a nurse's aide that comes in and takes you to the bathroom. You have someone who comes in and turns you to make sure you're not going to get bedsores. All of these people. They're coming in and changing your linens and bringing in your meals. Someone is preparing that food. The most that you can do now is answer the phone."

Gail: And that's a major accomplishment! That's interesting, Michael, because what I just flashed on when you said, "Well, my mother can do it" is that "R's" mother was almost 80 years old and could barely take care of herself. She was trying to take care of her dying son. But the fact of the matter was that she couldn't pick him up and put him on a portable toilet alongside the bed. Yes, she could fix his meals. Yes, she could go to the store and buy groceries, and she could come home and put them away and make little snacks. She could make phone calls for him. But she could not physically help him onto the toilet or into the shower; it was forgotten that she didn't have the capability. The other situation I just flashed on was the night that you and I did an intervention with "M". The questions we were asking him were "How would you feel if your 20-year old daughter had to wipe your fanny? If your 20-year-old daughter had to hold you up while you were in the shower?" -- meaning that she would have to strip down to some kind of a bathing suit and physically get in the shower with him and hold him up. All of a sudden, the light went on for him, and the embarrassment came up. Would he rather have his young daughter do that, or would he rather have an attendant who's being paid to do it? This is the kind of thing that people miss when they say they want to go home. If you've been in a hospital for a long period of time, you may not realize how weak you are or how much help you need. Even if you're capable of regaining your strength over a period of time, you don't see the bottom that you're in at the moment.

Michael: Because the bottom keeps moving away from you as you deteriorate. Like when you go from working to not working. You're still healthy enough to do something, perhaps a little bit of volunteer work. You know you can't go back to work because you physically can't get up at 7 o'clock in the morning and do all of the things you need to do and last through an eight-hour day. But you might be able to do half an hour, an hour, or even four hours of work.

Gail: That's a wonderful analogy.

Michael: We go through multiple stages. We die by inches; we don't die by yards. We die a little bit at a time, but, basically, it's all the same death. We just don't mourn each little bit the same way we mourn the last big one.

Gail: Yet, we do mourn losses all along the way. No longer being able to get up and go to work -- that's a major loss. Or no longer being able to walk or losing eyesight, they are major losses, too.

Michael: We mourn the big ones but sometimes miss the small ones. For example, you go from weighing 150 pounds to weighing 125, and you wonder what happened. Well, you lost 25 pounds. It didn't happen overnight. It happened over the course of the month, but were you paying attention?

Gail: Probably not.

Michael: And clearly, going from working to not working is a big thing.

Gail: Most people would agree. I'm reminded of another big one. I was with someone at the hospital who was telling me that he would be able to walk when he was released. Then came the realization that he lived on the second floor. There was no way he could bend his legs -- much less could his legs support his weight -- to get from the ground floor to his apartment. He lay there and cried. It was at that moment he realized how much he had deteriorated and that he was not going to be able to go home.

Michael: If you have a significant injury or illness that has caused you to be in the hospital, I understand that you lose as much as 25% of your strength after being in the hospital a week – regardless of your health status. Even if you're well from whatever has put you in the hospital, you've been significantly weakened.

Gail: I attended a wonderful seminar about what happens to a normal, otherwise healthy, 35-year-old male or female who has been hospitalized for 30 days with pneumonia. The deterioration goes on daily and hourly. Because you're so sedentary that your bowels cease to function, your urinary tract runs into problems, your lungs fill with fluid just from physically being in bed -- never mind if you have any other catastrophic problems. Just the immobility of lying in a hospital bed can create problem muscle and joint weakness.

Michael: And people who are in the hospital for a long period of time fail to realize that all of the people attending them are, in fact, preventing them from having an awareness of how disabled they have become. Now, granted, we're not going to force people to do things for themselves if they're incapable. But, in some respects, it almost needs to be pointed out, "We're doing things for you because you can't."

Gail: It doesn't mean that you won't ever be able to do things for yourself again -- another point that sometimes gets overlooked. But the fact of the matter is that sometimes the patient's fear -- the patient's hidden agenda -- is "My G-d, if I go into a facility, I'm never coming out!" That may not be the case. And if you don't ask, you may lie there wasting precious time on fear.

Michael: Many people who go into a skilled nursing facility believe that a physical therapist is going to come in and "make them better" - make them walk again. The therapist may check your ability to walk safely on your own, your gait, or the strength in your lower extremities. Could you use a walker? But the therapist is not going to make your legs better; he or she can only give directions. If your legs are not capable of doing what they're supposed to do, you are going to have to do some strengthening on your own. The therapist isn't going to give you an injection and say, "Your legs are all better now!"

Gail: Again, the hidden agenda! People assume, if they go home, that they are better and that they are going to survive. They make the jump, to "If I'm home, I'm okay! If I go into a facility, I'm dead!" You need to understand that isn't necessarily the case. It may be, but it may not be. And if you're not brave enough to check it out with the physician or the nurses that are taking care of you, then you're going to go through a lot of mental anguish.

Michael: Sometimes you may ask the question of someone who doesn't have the information -- the housekeeper, the nurse's aide, the roommate, or someone down the hall.

Gail: Or the minister, or the priest, or the rabbi.

Michael: You'll ask someone who doesn't have the information because you're testing -- you're testing the question out. The fact is that people who get this question asked of them should say, "Well, perhaps you should talk to your doctor about that," or "Perhaps you should ask your nurse."

Gail: And how do you get the doctor or the nurse to answer honestly? That can be a bigger problem than asking the question. I'll give you another example. I was at the hospital with my unconscious mother every day -- sometimes overnight -- and I was monitoring her physical condition quite closely. I wasn't just looking at the monitors up on the wall all the time; I was looking at her body. Was she passing urine? Was there blood in the urine? Were her bowels moving? Was she able to swallow? What was happening? One morning I walked in, lifted up the blankets, and found that her feet were black from the tip of her toes to her knees. I walked out and said to the nurse, "Excuse me, but what's going on?" It took 15 minutes of conversation with that nurse before she finally said to me -- in a very low voice, "Well, they're probably going to have to amputate her legs." Michael, it took 15 minutes! She was so uncomfortable with the directness of my question that it took her all that time to muster the courage to say those words. At that point, I looked at her, thanked her for the information, and said, "Please get my mother's physician on the phone" She did, and I said, "Doctor, I need to stop this," and he did. But I knew what I was doing, and I knew how to ask the question, while you or your family may not.

Michael: If you can stay with a physician or a nurse for 15 minutes, then maybe you will get the information. You probably have already experienced this with friends who come in and are so uncomfortable with the changes in you that they can't say anything. They may be smiling uncomfortably like they almost want to cry - or they do burst into tears. Perhaps you have said to yourself, "Wait a second. What's going on here? I'm taking care of everybody that comes into this room. I'm taking care of them, letting them off the hook by saying, 'You know what? I'm okay! Don't worry about me.'" But that's not what you want to say. You want to say, "Yes, it's a bitch! I can't walk anymore! I'm sad! Death is on its way!"

Gail: "And I'm scared, and I need your help. I need for you to be honest with me."

Michael: So, if you're the patient, we want you to be aware that people may not always be honest with you. It's not that they want to be dishonest. It's just a "little white lie." It's an act of omission. They are leaving out some important details such as, "Oh, by the way, we're going to have to amputate your legs."

Gail: When your legs are the least of your problems!

Michael: Right! What you need to say is "Get my physician on the phone! We need to stop this!"

Gail: That's right, Michael. There's going to be no more additional suffering!

Michael: Right! And if you're having trouble getting the treatment stopped, you need to grab the doctor or the nurse, and say, "I need you to be honest with me. I need you to tell me what's happening and verify what I'm seeing and feeling."

Gail: Yes -- again I'm going back to "A" -- because the fact of the matter is that the physician who made the decision to exfoliate her leg, as far as I'm concerned, committed an inhuman act. Because he knew what her underlining condition was and did not care.

Michael: I agree. Because what often happens is that it's forgotten that there is a whole body attached to those legs. Exfoliated! It sounds like something easy, like it's a product squeezed out of a tube.

Gail: When in fact, they were removing the dead skin from "A's" leg. Because she had a leg doctor, she didn't have a whole-body man. She had a leg man who was only interested in the leg. They forgot to check out the rest of her!

Michael: Right! And what you'll find in the hospital is that you've got the heart doctor; you've got the skin doctor.

Gail: You've got the nutritionist; you've got the

eye specialist.

Michael: It's like a delicatessen! It's as if no one is looking at the whole person. Just looking at the parts, and no one is driving the train. Well, you maybe, but no one told you!

Gail: I would prefer an approach that starts at the front where the mouth and the mind are, then moves down around the heart area. And only then begins to deal with everything else.

Message 2: Doing Nothing

Letting Go Isn't Giving Up

Michael: One of the things we've frequently talk-ed about is that giving up, stopping treatment, or choosing a different path is sometimes met with shame-inducing comments from either the healthcare provider or the family. "Oh, well, he's given up. They fought the battle and now they've given up," implying that you're a weak person for giving up and "doing nothing."

Gail: Yes, and it gets back to how you define "doing nothing." For many people, "doing noth-ing" means that one morning you wake up and you decide that you're tired. You're tired of the pain. You're tired of the depression. You're tired of the physical and emotional abuse that's been going on -- quite possibly for months and months and, in some cases, years. You want it to stop, but you're not quite sure how to stop it, or what will happen when you do stop it. So, let's talk about "doing nothing" -- the physical act of nothing. You have to think it through. You will probably want to discuss it with a close friend or confidant that you feel very comfortable with -- someone you feel will not shame you and that can truly understand your feelings. And you turn where?

Michael: You pick a friend or a family member - maybe not the primary family member - but you pick someone. You may say, "You know what? This present course is not working. I'm not comfortable with it, and I would like to do something different."

Gail: Yes, and, importantly, the person you choose has to be someone physically available, not three thousand miles away. Don't choose your brother in Philly. Choose someone who's around you all the time because you may not be able to get up, get in the car, and drive yourself to them. Don't choose someone who can't see with their own eyes what is happening to you. What is the usual reaction to "doing nothing" If you choose a good friend or a family member or, quite possibly, calling a minister, priest, or rabbi?

Michael: It usually ranges from "Oh, you don't want to do that," or "Isn't there something else they could do?" or "Haven't you tried___?" And they'll suggest some other option or treatment.

Gail: Often, you'll be secretly hoping that you're going to be talked out of "doing nothing."

Michael: You may be testing. Or you may be practicing the conversation with someone who appears to be "safe" so that you can then practice it with people who you feel are less "safe"-- such as a spouse, a lover, a mother, or a father.

Gail: A physician, perhaps.

Michael: Exactly.

Gail: So, you're practicing. You're going to use every opportunity you can. And, if you don't have a support group, then one of the suggestions, if you're still physically able, is that you seek out other people who are suffering from the same disease, or a similar disease, so that you can get an idea of what lies ahead by listening to others. Support groups and the benefits of support groups are the beginning of "doing nothing." I know that sounds strange, but you're really going at the fear and the frustration in a different way.

Michael: When doing nothing, you're actually doing something!

Gail: Exactly. Hopefully you're in some kind of support group and connected in some way with a group of people you can talk to and share your feelings -- your feelings of frustration, anger, disappointment, and sadness. Because you'll need to talk to someone about the kind of reactions you're going to get from doing nothing." Reactions like, "Oh, you don't want to do that yet!" "What do you mean? There's still treatment that can be done!" "Why would you want to give up?" "You have children!"

Michael: You may find that the person you've chosen isn't emotionally ready for "doing nothing" and may have strong emotional reactions of sadness and fear to what you're planning. They may break down. They may start crying. They may have a really hard time talking with you.

Gail: Their reaction of fear may turn into one of anger. They may get furious and scream, yell, and shout. They may turn away from you and have to leave the room. And in some cases, they will. And when they come back, they're going to want to talk about something else.

Michael: When you are actually dying, you choose very few people to be in your life. You don't have a lot of people around you because it's too hard. You find all too often that you have to take care of these people so that they, in turn, can be there for you. I've seen many situations where friends have been pushed away simply because the patient didn't have the energy to deal with them any longer. Perhaps you're already doing that with some of your friends. Nothing that overtly says, "I don't want to see you!" Instead, it's "Well, you know, you're busy, and I'm busy, and I've got all of these things to do. We can talk on the phone."

Gail: And the need to remove yourself from day-to-day life -- from day-to-day involvement in the here and now -- becomes a real issue for people who are terminally ill and are dying. You don't want to participate. Life becomes very narrow. You're busy with yourself. You're busy defending and protecting your peace and quiet, your privacy and your right to your own kind of life. The tendency then will be to say to good friends, "I don't want you around." You're going to do that in a variety of ways. In some cases, you may pick up the phone and say, "I can't have you in my life right now." That would be a very aggressive, very assertive person. All the way down to a lot of passive behavior which is, "Ah, well, I'd really like to see you, but I'm busy." Of course, the person on the other end of the phone is thinking, "Busy with what?" You don't have the courage yet to say to them, "I'm busy dying!"

Michael: If this is being read by a family member or a friend, it's important you understand this and not take it personally.

Gail: Yes, you have to get over your grieving in your own way and be willing to unemotionally approach the individual who's terminally ill with a clean slate.

Michael: Each person who is affected should be in their own support group. You should be involved with other families, friends, or significant others so that you have a place to put your feelings and to learn about this process and how to help yourself, your loved one, and others like you. Because you don't have the time or the energy to deal with all the emotions that are coming up -- for you and for them.

Gail: It isn't fair to them. I'm using the word "fair" because it's critical that family members hear that. Don't impose your wants, wills, and wishes on someone who is dying. When the patient, family members, and close friends are in their individual support groups, they can then start dealing appropriately with each other. The language will become clearer and cleaner.

Michael: The goal is to have clear, honest, truthful communication. Because when you're dying, the bottom line is that it's your body, your choice, your life, your death.

Gail: We're at the very early stages here. You've probably had multiple bouts of something already and moved past at least one set of aggressive treatments. You were able to tolerate the medications and tolerate the treatments, and you've had a good period of health. Maybe you're not as fully active as you used to be, but you've had some pleasures. And then it begins again. With each bout, the chances of recovery get less and less.

Now you're pushing away.

Michael: If you've reached the point where your treatment doesn't seem to be working, you may be looking for something different. Your focus is shifting to what you want to do next.

Gail: When you've decided what you want to do -- even if it's nothing -- you need to write it down. It's better if you write it -- that's a key point -- then practice with family and friends or whoever will listen to you. Wait for their reaction. Realize that a lot of the reaction that you're going to get is going to be very similar to the physician's. When you're ready, tell the physician you're going to do "nothing"! That you want it stopped. That you want to be able to direct the remainder of your life and do more pleasurable things -- even if it's just sitting some place listening to the birds and smelling the flowers. You want to be pain-free. You want to be clear and start saying your good-byes and making your final plans. Because the truth is you are doing something others probably can't comprehend.

Michael: Yes, and the fight to stop the disease and to make you healthy again -- that battle may be lost. But there are still battles you can win --

the battle to be comfortable, the battle to be pain-free, and the battle to have some control over the rest of your life.

Taking Care of Your Physician

Gail: The battle with your disease is lost, and your doctor may not bring this up to you.

Michael: The majority of physicians will not. Maybe that one doctor who has a special relationship with you will say, "Gosh, you know, we're not getting anywhere with this. But there is something else we can do. We can make sure that you're comfortable. We can keep you pain-free." You may or may not have that kind of direct communication with your doctor.

Gail: If you're cut off every time you try to talk with your doc, what can you do?

Michael: Well, let's assume you don't want to switch physicians at this point -- because that is an option. What I have seen with many physicians is that they either don't have the time or the space for the emotional reaction that's going to come up -- for them or for you, the patient. You have to bring it up in such a way as to allow the physician an opening -- a space to encourage the communication.

Gail: You need to get clear with your doctor that you don't want an hour or two of their time. You need to make sure he or she understands that they won't have to hold your hand for an hour while you go through the emotions of being told, "There's nothing more we can do for you." That's what the physician is afraid you're going to do -- that you're going to hold him or her captive while you do your emotional catharsis. So, you have to be very clear that you've come to grips with your situation. Yes, you're sad, but you've accepted it, and what you'd like from your doctor is just a clear explanation of what you can expect from now on.

Michael: One significant suggestion is that -- if it's appropriate and you feel comfortable -- you take someone with you to the doctor's office.

Gail: You've absolutely got to have someone along with you at all times, whenever you reach a certain place in your disease, especially late-stage/end-stage. We can't emphasize this too much.

Michael: And, it should be someone who can handle the emotions that may be coming up for you. Someone who will not abandon you when the physician actually has to leave the room. Someone who will make sure that you're not alone.

Gail: Asking a nurse to stay with you would be appropriate if you have a relationship with one of the nurses in the office.

Michael: Or you might bring your therapist, or your counselor, or someone else you trust to process the information -- someone who can hear what the doctor says and discuss it with you later.

Gail: They can just sit with you, take notes, and listen to you afterwards. They can feed back to you exactly what the physician really said. Remember to let this person have a good cry; whatever is said will be hard on them, too.

Michael: The other thing that could be done is similar to an intervention where you actually set up a patient conference with the physician -- something they can schedule to be longer than the usual appointment.

Gail: Let's go back to the subject of changing physicians for a moment. Generally, the first appointment with a new physician is, in fact, a consultation. Say you're going for a second opinion. You as the patient want to know how far along you are in your disease. You choose a physician, you ask for a consultation, you take all of your paperwork -- blood tests, chest x-rays, etc., anything else you have. You take along that support person that we mentioned earlier, and you ask for direct and candid conversation. That's another possibility. Most people, however, are not this assertive as patients. What we're suggesting isn't always possible because of your personality, your lifestyle -- perhaps, you're a bit timid. Taking along a support person to any appointment is an excellent idea, especially when you have a life-threatening disease. Anything to help you speak up for yourself. And to remember what was said. (Remember, support person, you're there to listen and not to speak for the patient unless you're asked.)

Michael: Because you may be so emotionally overwhelmed that you won't hear everything.

The information is going to be coming at you in waves. You hear the crest of the wave, but you may not hear everything that was said after that. You may hear the next crest of the wave, but you may not hear the details. A third party can really help you process the information after you've left the doctor's office, or on the way home, or even the next day. It's equally important to go to the doctor's prepared with written questions or statements that you want to make. You need to be prepared both beforehand and afterwards to deal with all the information.

Gail: It's also extremely important for you to ask for the spelling of any term, medication, or procedure the doctor has used if you are not familiar with it, or you want to look it up. Be very clear so that you can then go to your pharmacist, computer, a medical book, or ask someone to make sure you understand everything that was said to you. The physician will tend to move the language up -- out of your range. The more you know, the less your fear and the greater your control.

Whose Trip Is This, Anyway?

Michael: That gets back to the subject of your responsibility for managing your disease. The information is out there -- if you know how to ask for it. If you understand what's going on, you can take control and move up to the next stage, which can bring many positive changes.

Gail: It's going to free you. There's going to be an emotional release which is going to bring you inner peace. Because when you don't have the information, your fears can cause you to tensely hold your body -- and that takes a tremendous amount of energy. Knowledge will ease that. To summarize, know that when you start bringing up the subject of "doing nothing," you're going to get a negative reaction. "You can't do that! I love you!"

Michael: Others are going to impose upon you their judgments, shame, guilt, fear, and denial when you say things like, "I'm going to stop treatment."

Gail: And what is their "hidden agenda"?

Michael: Their agenda is to reduce their own fears; after all, they are going to lose you.

Gail: Let's go back, then, to talking about "letting go," which is generally perceived by others as a negative. You, on the other hand, instinctively know that "letting go" is a positive for you -- even though you may not be able to verbalize it. It gives you freedom. You can say what you want. You can be free with your emotions, and you can let go of your fear, your frustration, and your pain. What emerges to family, friends, and physicians is a very clear human being who doesn't have time for the lies or the "B.S." You've shifted. Maybe the rest of the world hasn't, but you've shifted! Remember, it has to begin with you if it's going to happen at all.

Michael: Most people are afraid of being left out of your life. It's hard for them to understand that dying is a private and personal trip that we do alone -- or with very few people.

Gail: I'm reminded that some people who die seem to wait until others leave the room. That's the clearest evidence to me of how much dying is very personal. People seem to wait until a family member goes to the restroom or goes out for a cigarette or down for a cup of coffee.

Michael: Do you know why? Because they have not let go of the patient.

Gail: There's something about the energy of the individual that's holding them here.

Michael: Yes! It doesn't always happen that way, but it happens very frequently in our experience. If the family is just not ready, the patient will wait for an opportunity and leave the planet when nobody's around. When the energy is not holding them back.

Gail: That's very interesting. A lot of people are afraid of dying alone. We've heard that comment. They are afraid of not having someone present that they love and care for. So, there's a mixed message going on. "I'm afraid to be alone, but I won't die until I am alone." In reality, they often choose to wait until the person they love is out of the room.

Michael: Many families are upset because they

missed being there at the moment of death. I often relate that many of us in healthcare believe that the patient chooses to leave at a time that's going to be easiest for them. While you as a family member may want to be there, they may not want you there. They may feel uncomfortable in leaving while you're present. They may wait until you go to the bathroom. They may wait until you leave for the evening. I tell families not to feel bad but to understand it was the patient's choice.

Gail: And this is all ages and all sexes.

Michael: Absolutely!

Gail: And all cultures. This is not an isolated incident. It occurs over and over again. We apparently are being told that some of our fears and apprehensions about the moment of our death will not necessarily come true.

Michael: Right. And another aspect of this is when people say, "Well, you know, they are just waiting for their brother to show up from Pittsburgh." The brother shows up, and that night the patient dies. Everyone is wondering, "How did he hold on until then?" If you can hold on until a certain time, then the opposite may be true -- that you can let go at a certain time.

Gail: As a family member, it's also important for you to realize that you cannot control the patient's wishes. You can try, but you're going to find out that it doesn't work. You can't say "Mother's coming, wait for her!" Because the patient has already decided who they want to wait for and who they don't. They may not really want to see Mom. Whatever the reason, they just don't wait-either because it is too painful or because everything has already been cleaned up. Then, of course, the shame and the blame falls, "Oh, my God, wasn't it a shame that he or she couldn't wait for so-and-so to get here?" Well, they didn't have the need. The living had the need.

Michael: That is a real concern. Just as the ritual that goes on after a person is dead is not for the patient; it's for the living. The same is true for those thoughts and feelings that come up around "Oh, I wish I'd gotten there!" Well, it's difficult for people. Take yourself off the hook. Family members and friends don't have control. Unless the choice is to keep a person on a life support system until that brother comes in from Pittsburgh.

Gail: Even if you're on a ventilator, you pick

your own time. It's amazing -- ventilator or no ventilator -- people have been removed from ventilators and not succumbed. That is very definitely one of the hidden agendas to remember when we talk about the patient's "hidden agenda."

Suicide by Any Other Name

Gail: Let's talk about suicide. One of the things that we hear often is that someone -- particularly one who has had a devastating blow -- will say, "I'm going to kill myself." Of course, my favorite reply to that -- and I still use it is, "So do you have your stash? Do you have your drugs? Do you have your plastic bag? Where are you going to do it? Who is going to find you? What kind of a mess will they walk into? Is someone going to help you or are you brave enough to do it yourself?" And just talk it through. Because 99 times out of 100 all the person wants to do is talk about lt. Are you going to use prescription medication or go down to the street corner and try to make contact with a drug dealer? If you're inexperienced, that can be a frightening trip! Working this is an important part, but it's a part that's rarely talked about. It's all about giving people a place to talk, to try it out, to hear how it sounds. Watching people light up when they realize that it's possible to talk about this, to be understood, and to still be safe.

Michael: Because no one is available that will allow them to talk about it, they think that suicide is the only way out. It may be the fastest way out, but it's not the only way out. If you want to leave the planet, you're going to leave.

Gail: But they don't know that. They haven't experienced enough people around them dying. And I mean "experienced." Being present at the time-up to and including death. We talk about two kinds of suicide. First, there is the deliberate act -- which is what people want to talk about. "I'm going to get a gun." "I'm going to take pills." "I'm going to slash my wrists." And now they think there is Physician Assisted Suicide or PAS, which we will go into in a moment. There are other kinds of suicide, which you and I have seen. "I'm going to stop my meds. I'm going to stop eating. I'm tired. I have had enough pain. There is no quality to my life."

Michael: The folks who believe in physician-assisted suicide seem to see suicide as their only way out, as their only option in terms of having control over their death. In actuality, all that they have controlled is the time of their death rather than the amount of suffering they're going to experience. It's "I'm going to die on Tuesday at 10:00, and I'm going to stage the whole thing in such a manner that this is when I'm going to check out." They don't even call it suicide anymore. They refer to it by the euphemism "medical aid in dying."

Gail: And the reason that they want to control "checking themselves out" is because they're afraid of what's coming.

Michael: Because they don't want to go through the whole experience. They want the skip the dying part because they want to avoid suffering.

Gail: We have seen there are two reasons for people wanting to die by their own hand. One is the total need for control. The other reason is fear. Being afraid there will be no one there to take care of you. Being afraid they're going to be in a tremendous amount of pain. Afraid that they're going to be ugly, even that they will smell.

Michael: Some people are also afraid that there will be somebody there to care for them, and they don't want that particular somebody.

Gail: You don't want that person there at the moment of your death because you don't want them involved. They've given you problems your whole life, and you just flat don't want them there! It's almost like you're punishing them. And you're looking for a fast exit. "F" was afraid that his alcoholic mother was going to step in at the last minute and not be sober enough to do for him what was appropriate. And she was it; he didn't have any other immediate family. And he was afraid. From the moment of his birth and for his entire life, her alcoholism had prevented her from caring for him. So why should he trust that she was going to be there at the end of his life and help him die? He had a lot of real fears around that.

Michael: And he had such anger about how he was brought up that there was no way he was going to be obligated to, or dependent on, anyone.

Gail: He was young. He didn't understand that he had other ways to handle his problem with dependency. So, in his case, he was dealing with a limited amount of life experience. With most of the people we are in contact with, that's not the case. They are a little bit older. They have really thought it through, and they don't want to suffer. Flat out, they do not want to consciously suffer! We have seen a deliberate act of suicide where someone has taken their own life, and we have seen people do what I call a "quiet suicide," which is generally when they decide to stop treatment. I'd like to hear more from you about some of the options that people have regarding care. The fear they've got about what's going to happen to them physically may not be totally alleviated, but it can certainly be softened.

Michael: The primary thing is that they have to have a positive, clear relationship with their health care provider.

Gail: You mean they have to trust their health care provider.

Michael: Yes. They have to trust that person to take care of them and be responsive to what their needs are now and at the time when they are, in fact, dying -- up to and including death. For example, they have to trust that person to ensure that they have adequate pain management regardless of whether they are at home or in a facility. "Tell me, doctor, that I'm not going to be in pain! Tell me that you are going to ensure that there is going to be enough medication, either in my house or in a prescription, that's going to ensure that whoever's caring for me -- whether it's an agency that's coming out or my mother that's here -- that person is going to have access to medication. That given enough of it I will be pain free. And that I can keep upping it until I no longer have pain." That is a totally reasonable request!

Gail: And if you hear the words, "But we don't want you to become addicted" run like hell! Because that is a physician or a nurse that is not conscious enough of the need or of the standard of care for taking care of terminally ill patients.

Michael: It may not necessarily be the physician that says "addiction." It may also be you who thinks you're going to become addicted. It may be that you have a problem with the issue addiction. You may, in fact, be in recovery yourself, and you may have a problem with taking mood-altering drugs. You may have a problem with the fact that you need lots of it, that you crave it, or that you sense that you will crave it.

Gail: So, then there's the guilt about enjoying it, needing it, or using it if you're someone in recovery from alcohol or drugs.

Michael: One of the ways you can relieve some of your guilt is by saying, 1) "My doctor's prescribing this!" 2) "Being in pain is not enjoying life!" and 3) "I'm not going to live long enough to become addicted." In actuality, less than a half a per cent of all patients become addicted. It's an unrealistic, unnecessary, fear.

Gail: We're talking about your abusing yourself with drugs and alcohol. It's important because it's crucial whether you are conscious or unconscious. In our society we remove ourselves from pain with drugs and alcohol. The people around you will probably want you to sober up. A lot of people don't want to sober up or quit smoking. If you have been an abuser your whole life, you may want to die using drugs -- whether it's alcohol, narcotics, or cigarettes. And I believe you have the right to do it as long as you understand the consequences of your behavior. You will be forced to sober up for short periods of time because of hospitalization. You're going to get a taste of being sober whether you want to be or not. This discussion is for people who are sober, those in recovery, and for those who are not sober.

Michael: This discussion is for people who are conscious. You can continue to self-medicate yourself and still be somewhat conscious.

Gail: Yes, you can. And you can be more conscious by feeling your emotions and going through the experience.

Michael: It's different from taking something that's been prescribed by the physician to prevent you from feeling physical pain.

Gail: The basic issue is still a matter of doing your best to deal confidently with your fears and pain. This is in part a function of the trust you have in your physician. Your stability is often tied to your relationship with your doctor. Unfortunately, in some people's experience with physicians, they find a lot of excuses, stammering, and avoidance around dealing directly with a dying patient. So when you say "trust" and you say "confidence" and you say "a long established relationship with a physician," those are the key words. And you've absolutely got to get a positive response from that physician.

Michael: And with managed care and the changes now in healthcare, you have to work extra hard to establish a relationship with your doctor. It's unfortunate that you have to work so hard. But, you know, people have been given an opportunity for years and years to develop a relationship with their doctor, and they have chosen not to. They go in and they let things happen to them; they let things be done to them without having any say. It's kind of like "Walk on top of me. Just walk right over me. I'm not here. I don't matter. My opinion doesn't count." Too often the patient is too intent on pleasing their physician.

Gail: Just prior to her death, one patient's mother made a request to the primary physician for pain medication -- at the house. And she was informed by the physician that he didn't like to do that until it was absolutely necessary. Now, how much more necessary does it have to get? He didn't like the idea that she had pain medication there because there was a possibility that she could assist her daughter's suicide. And that was the truth! The fact of the matter is that the patient had enough medication; she had been saving up for months to do the job. All she was after was a morphine pump. She wanted it there in the event she went into severe physical agony. She wanted to be able to quickly hook up the line instead of having to wait 12 hours for the nurse to get a hold of the physician, to be able to get an order to the pharmacist, for the delivery service to get from the pharmacist to her home, and then to wait for a home health care nurse to hook up the line. She had thought it through.

Michael: That problem rarely occurs if hospice is involved. Did they have hospice involved?

Gail: Yes, they did. But the doctor would not let go of his control of the patient. The patient was not in any condition to be asked anything; and the physician was dealing with the mother.

Michael: So, the mother was specifically asking, "I want a PCA pump." That's a Patient Controlled Analgesia pump.

Gail: And "I want it in the house." The physician had already told her that when her daughter went into end-stage, she would be in severe pain.

So, she had already been flagged. And grinding up aspirin and slipping it under her daughter's tongue wasn't going to do it. Even the morphine, although it helped a little, was going to become inadequate.

Michael: More reasons you need to have good communication with the people involved in your dying.

Gail: I want to reiterate a point I made earlier because I know it's rarely discussed. The fact of the matter is that there are two forms of suicide -- active and passive. I see the word "suicide" as the socially unacceptable active form. But stopping your medication, stopping your treatment, stopping eating are passive forms of suicide that no one wants to talk about -- as a suicide. They'll talk about it in other ways. But they won't say, "Oh, well, he killed himself." Well, let me tell you something, we know any number who killed themselves because they got to the point where they looked at their physician and they said, "No more!"

Michael: Absolutely.

Gail: They consciously made the decision to stop treatment and let Nature, G-d, Spirit -- whatever word you want to use -- whatever your religious belief system is -- take over and let them go naturally. I do not see that as any more or less a form of suicide. To me it is suicide. It is a conscious act.

Michael: We've talked about that earlier in terms of stopping the aggressive care -- your chemo therapy or radiation or whatever -- and starting the comfort measures of palliative care. You're actually doing "something."

Gail: When you stop, you're not really stopping. You're only stopping one approach and starting something else. And that's the language that the patient needs to use. "I've decided to stop what I've been doing and let nature take its course."

Palliative Care

Michael: Before we go much further, we should again explain that palliative care is specialized medical care for people living with serious illness. At its best, it is a team effort of trained physicians, nurses, and social workers who focus on providing relief from the symptoms and the stress of serious illness. The goal is to improve the quality of life for the patient, their families and friends. This form of care can be offered at any point from diagnosis of a serious health condition until death.

Gail: Yes, hospice is actually the end-stage version of palliative care. Sometimes the terms are used interchangeably. But they should not be since it is often appropriate to have palliative care way before one is dying -- in some cases years before. However, a real problem today is a shortage of personnel in these fields. And, unfortunately, both the medical and insurance communities have not known what to do with it, often pushing patients into hospice prematurely and sometimes unnecessarily. This can cause confusion and desperation on the part of the patient. And this can lead to the patient wanting to talk about suicide.

Physician-Assisted Suicide

Michael: As we know, physician-assisted suicide, which is sometimes called physician-aided dying, is a hot and controversial topic in end-of-life care. The reason is two-fold, patients do not want to suffer, and they want to control the outcome. Most people if asked about the issue in theory-- regardless of their health status -- will freely state that if it gets too bad, they would want to end it.

Gail: This is a common response with competent individuals.

Michael: The trouble is that it is not easy -- perhaps intentionally so. One doesn't wake up one day and decide to die. It is a significant process, one that will require effort and consistency on your part. The law has only been passed in a few states and requires not one but two physicians stating you are terminally ill and have the mental capacity to kill yourself. The request must be made twice in writing with a gap of 1-2 weeks. Then the physicians have to be willing to write the prescription and a pharmacist will have to be willing to fill it. You must pay for the drugs, as your insurance will not. A hospice referral is encouraged to help ensure you are thoroughly familiar with the alternatives. The laws are based on the acceptance of a legal fiction that killing oneself under physician-assisted suicide is not suicide. The cause of death can be listed as the underlying disease, not the drug, and a variety of life insurance and other proceeds are not invalidated. For many, a possible stigma might be avoided.

Gail: And you must ask for the referral. No doctor, nurse, social worker will give you that referral. And remember, all of this is required to take place before you lose the capacity to physically and mentally complete the process. Your family or a surrogate decision maker cannot make the choice for you and cannot assist you in the process of taking the medication. The law requires you to have "the physical and mental ability to self-administer the drug." "Self-administer means a qualified individual's affirmative, conscious, and physical act of administering and ingesting the aid-in-dying drug to bring about his or her own death." And, to top it off, one can't depend on the laws that are in place as they are constantly being challenged in court. It's a complicated issue, and, not surprisingly, there is no shortage of reference material, discussions, and opinions on the internet. I think that at this point we need to talk about Option #3, which we see as a powerful and highly appropriate alternative which has not received the attention, publicity, and discussion it deserves. Unlike physician-assisted suicide, Option #3 does not require weeks of waiting and detailed paperwork.

Option #3 - Assisted Slumber

Michael: Yes. Up until now, the medical field has kept pretty quiet about something they call "continuous controlled sedation" or "palliative sedation" or "continuous palliative sedation therapy" or "sedation for intractable distress in the dying" which is perhaps the most significant and least complicated option for patients to choose when uncontrolled, intolerable, or unrelenting suffering is unacceptable to the individual, and a state of continuous sleep is the desired alternative. It's important that the intent is to relieve unendurable suffering, including existential, and not to hasten the patient's death. People should know of this choice when alternatives such as comfort care, hospice care, palliative care, and pain control are no longer effective.

Gail: This is for end-stage patients and does not require legal permission -- just have it added to your POLST documents or your Durable Power of Attorney for Health Care (or Advanced Health Care Directive). You should talk this over with the people you love, partners, close friends, family. This is a part of hospice and is used when nothing more can be done. Discuss this with your primary, your palliative, and your hospice physicians. After all, don't most people say, "Personally, I'd just like to go peacefully in my sleep!" or "As for dying, I'd just like to sleep through the whole thing!" How about you?

Michael: One possible addition to your POLST under Additional Orders might read: "If I am suffering inconsolably, I request my physician arrange medication for ASSISTED SLUMBER (Continuous Controlled Sedation) So I can sleep to avoid suffering and maximize comfort until my death."

Message 3: Hidden Agendas

Yours and Theirs

Michael: It's very important to explore what, if any, are your "hidden agendas" because they can cause you to suffer unnecessarily. 1) You may not understand why, but you might not ask for help; 2) you may wait for help from a walk-in (a stranger who has come into your life to help you do closure); or 3) you may want to die. Whatever you want is OK. Dying is OK. Let's explore a little and try to determine if you have any "hidden agendas." The key is to know your own agendas so you can disarm them and keep them from hurting you. To bring them into your awareness so you can control them as opposed to their controlling you.

Gail: We can have all kinds of hidden agendas. We can have a hidden agenda that says, "Well, you know, if I were to get well, I'd probably only go back to doing the same thing that I did before.

And those behaviors may be what got me here in the first place. So maybe I don't really want to look into getting rid of alcohol, drugs, smoking, obesity, sexual addiction, or whatever."

Michael: Maybe your family doesn't know about your hidden agendas. You're going to keep them private, and you're going to die because you don't really want to live unless you can hang on to them -- those things that you really don't want to talk about.

Gail: There can be a lot of shame around hidden agendas -- a tremendous amount of shame.

Michael: Living a lie.

Gail: Exactly! We have seen shame so strong that it can actually drive your will to die. In truth, however, people feel shame just for having a disease -- any disease. Even though on the outside you are talking a good game of fighting the disease and wanting to live, the actual inside talk can be a result of society's prejudice, and such thoughts as "I'm not worthy. I'm a filthy, horrible person."

Michael: "And so I'm going to continue my self-destructive behavior." This is the kind of thinking that can drive your disease.

Gail: All along no one else is probably aware of this agenda. The physician who is treating you, the nurse who is taking care of you, the parent who has flown in to help you. No one realizes. No one talks about what's going on inside of you. They're afraid to ask. It may be more than they, in truth, really want to deal with.

Michael: A good support group -- particularly a therapy group -- will help you bring those issues to the surface.

Gail: It will not cure you of your disease, but it will help you discharge the energy behind that shame so that you can move into some thing else -- something more positive with less stress on your body.

Michael: There's a difference between a support

group and a therapy group. Sometimes people think they're getting therapy in a support group when actually all that's really going on is that they are acquiring information or education. The issues never get worked through unless they've dealt with it in a therapy setting. Unfortunately, support groups may promote you staying stuck -- and keep you from making progress in dealing with deeper problems.

Gail: When you get into your group, you find that you can't be without it. You find that it's the safest -- the most honest -- place to be.

Michael: Exploring the deep, dark secrets in your life is difficult. It's difficult whether you're sick or healthy.

Gail: Take, for example, when a family lie is exposed. I'll never forget the time a woman talked about how she had been molested by her father. For the first time, she was able to discuss it -- to talk about the fact that it had occurred, that her father is still in her life, but that the incidents are never discussed between them. She was able to look at how she treats other people in her life in the same way that she treats her father. And how that pain and shame might be driving her cancer. With that in mind, this is a good time to take a minute and talk about what happens in a therapy group.

Michael: Every form of conversation is permitted and encouraged. Great efforts are made to make it clear that you don't have to hide and lie about your life, that judgment and criticism are not allowed.

Gail: It's always amazing -- when you feel safe -- how the words just fall out of your mouth. It's like "Oh, my G-d, you mean I can talk about that?" And you find yourself so much lighter, with your stress reduced and maybe a stronger immune system or recuperative powers. And who knows? You might live longer! Long-term survivors are very often group members.

Michael: Often someone will say to us, "Oh, my "G-d", you have a group of dying patients! How depressing!" "Who'd want to be involved with those people!" And yet, how many evenings did those in the group say, "Did we ever laugh tonight! We had a good laugh about___!" The humor used in group is actually freeing. While that type of often dark humor may not be acceptable outside the group, it certainly is acceptable inside. Because it's safe there. Being permitted to discuss or disclose anything that's weighing on you is very freeing.

Gail: The reason for revealing hidden agendas is to make it lighter for you.

Michael: To lighten a burden that may have been there for 25 years. Say, perhaps, you've been unfaithful and never told your partner.

Gail: Or you were a recreational drug user, or you liked to cross-dress, or you're a kleptomaniac. The most tragic one I can remember is someone who had to go into another personality or alter-ego. He was bisexual and unable to function unless he literally became another human being. And that human being was crazy. This individual had allowed himself to be institutionalized again and again because the only way he could act out his homosexuality was to become this other crazy personality. And this other personality killed him in the end because he was so ashamed of it that he didn't take care of himself -- an extreme, unusual use of a hidden agenda.

Hidden Agendas -- Insurance

Michael: Another possible hidden agenda is your expectations of your insurance company.

Gail: Yes, no matter how much information you get, a hidden agenda is "These people are supposed to take care of me. They are supposed to keep me pain free. They are supposed to keep me clean. They are supposed to make sure that I'm in a tolerable situation."

Michael: That's your expectation of your insurance company. But the insurance company has its own agenda, which is usually dollar driven; while you as the patient have your own fantasy about your care, which is that all the things you need will be in place for you when you need them.

Gail: And it's not bad or wrong to have those beliefs. It's just that you're going to be horribly disappointed when you want to have what you assumed your insurance was going to provide -- and then it doesn't live up to your expectations.

Michael: What you're bringing up is another aspect of denial. Being in denial about what is available to you from your insurance company or Medicare or Medicaid. Not being in denial requires that you ask questions early on so that you can make choices.

Gail: And you have to be willing to hear the answers to those questions.

Michael: Right, unless you're in denial. If you're in denial, you can't! It prevents you from getting the information that's going to help you later.

Gail: And that denial is found even in the health care community, which often doesn't want to think of you as terminally ill -- even when it's clear you are.

Michael: Yes, and, of course, that generally depends on your financial situation. If you have excellent insurance or if you have the means to pay for the treatment, the system is then geared towards treating -- and treating aggressively -- as long as the dollars are there and as long as spending those dollars can be reasonably justified.

Gail: What happens in the system when you're totally indigent and you find yourself on welfare -- and you're a young person? What kind of an attitude are you going to be confronted with?

Michael: It depends on whether you have family members who are able to provide some of the day-to-day care. That they can make sure that you're kept clean, that you're fed, that you're safe in your environment. For example, you may be allowed to continue aggressive treatment like radiation and chemotherapy, without any question. That is, if you have family and friends who are willing to make sure that you have a place to stay. However, if you have no place to stay and no means to pay for such a place, then you're going to be encouraged to explore options that you may not necessarily want to explore. As a state or county supported patient, you may feel that you don't really have a choice. You may feel that you have to choose either very aggressive treatment in the hospital, or very little treatment, or palliative care, or just comfort measures in a place such as a hospice. You can also have hospice in your home, but that assumes you have a capable caregiver or that you are capable of providing care for yourself.

Gail: Or you have financial resources and the ability to collect and manage those caretakers that come into your home. The big point here is that if you have the resources and you have the family members in place, the industry then is going to keep you on the path of aggressive treatment. They're going to make all kinds of recommendations and suggestions.

Michael: And in the beginning, if you have good insurance, they're going to get very aggressive. If you don't have good insurance, they may drag their feet. If you don't have any insurance at all, you have to qualify as indigent to get on a state or county program.

Gail: In a lot of ways, you'd almost be better off on "the system" of county, state, and federal programs because then you're going to learn how to be aggressive.

Michael: And you will be praised for taking that route because, strangely, it shows you're compliant. If you're compliant with the expectations of the healthcare industry, if you're compliant with your physician, they'll give you a number of options to steer you towards the aggressive treatment. Because importantly that's considered "doing something." And for them, doing something is better than what they consider to be doing nothing. Doing something gives them some sense of purpose, some sense of helping, of instilling hope, of giving people a chance. "That is what we have at our disposal; so that is what we're going to give you." When you pursue aggressive treatment, you're praised. "Good job! You're being compliant. We're happy with this!" Even though sometimes aggressive treatment is very uncomfortable. If you're reading this and you have cancer, or chronic heart failure, or some other chronic life-threatening disease, then you've probably already experienced some form of aggressive treatment. It is unlikely that you were given the choice to do nothing at the very beginning.

Gail: Yes, you have already gone through a certain amount of pain. You've already been told "We got it all. You're doing fine. Your chances of survival are very good. We only lose 10% of our patients; the other 90% go on to lead a full life." This is the kind of language you're going to hear. But when the patient crosses the line, and the physician accepts that you are terminal, what happens then to the language?

Michael: The language to the patient may not

change. But the language to the family from the physician and the language between healthcare providers may change dramatically.

Gail: At that point they are privately giving each other little signals. They're having conversations that are obviously not designed for you. Because there is an illusion that if they're direct with you, you are going to lose hope and die, or you are going to lose hope and go into severe depression, or you are going to kill yourself.

Michael: Or you will no longer be compliant with treatment and are not going to come in and see the physician, are not going to go for this other treatment, or have this antibiotic, or have this, this, and this --which are all things that cost money.

Gail: The healthcare provider knows -- from the kind of insurance or aid that the patient has -- exactly how much can be billed. Every policy has a limit. Someone from the insurance company will call the physician's office or the hospital and say, "We've got a million dollars on this particular problem. This is all the patient can have!" Unfortunately, some providers are going to milk it.

Michael: That may be a harsh statement, but the truth is that it clearly occurs in some situations where people are not necessarily looking after your best interests, even though they say they are by trying all of these things, searching out every avenue, and investigating, and diagnosing, and testing.

Gail: This makes sense in the earlier stages, but in the later stages, when these private conversations start up between practitioners, "There really isn't a lot of hope in this treatment, but we've got to look active to the family. We've got to look active to the patient." Sometimes it seems dollar-driven, but it usually appears that it is done to keep you busy and feeling attended to.

Hidden Agendas -- Physicians

Michael: It's the physician's job at this point to keep you busy. Because, as we pointed out, for them doing something is better than doing nothing. Doing something also avoids discussion about the prognosis -- death. That's the physicians' hidden agenda.

Gail: Again, that taps into their fear of failure.

Michael: Right! In earlier times, physicians had very little at their disposal to help you. They sat with you; they observed you; they saw what was going on. But now they have machines, and they have computers, and they have CAT scans and MRI's, and all sorts of things that can give them more information about what's going on in the body. But it doesn't give them any information at all about what you want. The only way you get that is for them to ask you -- or for you to tell them.

Gail: It used to be that the patient had to be involved because of the physician's limited resources.

Michael: Right! What the physician would do is ask you what is going on. "What are you feeling? What are your sensations?" They would ask, "Does this hurt? Does that hurt?" Whereas now many physicians don't trust you because you're not a computer or a lab report.

Gail: Not only that, the assumption is that you are over-reacting to whatever symptoms the computer is showing. I also find that many physicians simply don't want to get involved. In the past, physicians would stay with you until you died; there would be an intimacy going on between you and the physician. I'm wondering if we're not walking around with a belief system that the physician is still going to stay with us until we die -- that the physician is going to be our ally. When, in fact, at end-stage the physician usually disappears or has been replaced with a stranger. Whether it's because of fear of failure, or fear of their own mortality, just plain social awkwardness, lack of training, fee schedules, or hospital policy, they get scarce and leave. After all, the nurse can take care of you.

Michael: And, remember, primary physicians, for all intents and purposes, have lost their function in this scenario. Because they are there to fix or repair something that is no longer fixable or repairable. Because of their training, they may feel there is nothing more they can do -- that what is needed is a nurse, social worker, friend or someone to sit with the patient. They believe that there are other people they can still do something for. What happens is that the physician disappears at the end-stage really because they've lost their role. In fact, I don't think they want the role. But there is a level of frustration I've seen with some physicians when they wish they could do something. Really, if they are doing anything in terms of easing suffering, relieving pain, taking care of symptoms -- those kinds of activities -- then they are doing something. They're being compassionate, and they're doing what you need at that time. But they may feel that they aren't doing anything because they're no longer treating the disease. And, remember, beating the disease is the most important thing for them.

Gail: And they are not allowed to participate in the death. Society does not allow them to help you die. That is a taboo subject. So, they must be able to transition from doing something to doing nothing, and they don't know how to do that. Doing nothing is not an option. They must do something, and we don't allow them to transition from the practice of medicine to the good death. These days a palliative care or a hospice physician will be in charge.

Michael: Yes, in today's world, it would be extremely rare for your primary physician to orchestrate the good death.

Gail: By that we mean allowing you to transition out of this life with minimal pain and suffering. Since the physician can't participate in that, they walk away. Our belief as patients, however, is that they are always going to be there -- that the physician will take care of us until we close our eyes. That's the belief we are walking around with. It has been said over and over in our groups. The fact of the matter is that this is not going to be the case. This is a very important piece of information. In the group, where there are multiple deaths, the other members always say, "Oh, my G-d, they're right!" Because they know that the physician was absent at the time of their friend's death. The physician was nowhere to be found. But the average person doesn't get that opportunity. Many people die alone, and it becomes a singular event instead of a multiple event. Their only experience is what they've seen on television and in the movies.

Michael: Because the majority of people in our culture, especially those below middle age, have not witnessed a death personally -- have not been personally involved or present.

Gail: What also happens is you can become upset with those you perceive have their own hidden agendas. Your energy level is wasted on the anger, the frustration, and the resentment you may feel toward your physicians, your insurance company, caregivers or any number of others. So, in the latter days of your life -- or the latter weeks or months -- you may waste a tremendous amount of energy in the wrong direction. You may ruminate or go over and over again in your head about what you believe you were cheated out of.

Michael: And you're not wrong for having those feelings. Just as your insurance company and society isn't responsible for everything you may need.

Gail: Calling a case manager at your insurance company should start the appropriate actions and activate a different kind of action and feelings about your case.

Michael: Absolutely. It clearly requires that you be a conscious participant. Sometimes when you start talking about this, other concerns are brought up, such as, "What if the insurance company says no"? or "If I can't have this, what will I do?"

Gail: Some people think it's better to be in the dark or blissfully ignorant rather than an aware participant.

Michael: It's like the woman who feels something during a breast examination in the shower. She thinks there's something there. How long will she wait before she actually goes into action? What goes on in her mind? What happens? Does she think, "Oh, G-d, I've got to see the doctor!" Does she immediately go into action and know exactly what she needs to do, or does she have some doubt about the lump even being there? "Maybe it was just the way I did it this morning. I've done it before, and I've not felt anything there. I'll wait until I take another shower."

Gail: Or fear will just put it out of her mind.

Michael: And she says, "No, I can't deal with that right now!" Because what happens when you find a lump, or you notice something? Immediately you have to discount it. You have to go into what we call a "healthy denial" before you can start dealing with scary information. If you start thinking immediately of the worst, then you will be paralyzed. Something happens during that period from getting a diagnosis of a possible terminal disease or "The News," to realizing that you need to get instructional information, and then actually getting it? That something is denial. It's often a fear of appearing foolish.

Gail: As long as you take some action at the appropriate point, then that denial is healthy. That's what people do. That's their normal reaction in finding out. It's letting it go on too long that puts you in a very dangerous situation -- in more ways than one.

Michael: There's no way we can over-emphasize the importance of being proactive. Just as you need to be proactive with the disease, you need to be proactive with everything else.

Hidden Agendas -- Who's Responsible?

Gail: I sometimes get very confused about what is the patient's responsibility and what is the healthcare industry's responsibility. What I'm seeing is that no one wants to take responsibility.

Michael: Exactly!

Gail: It's not a matter of being in denial. It's a matter of not understanding. For some reason, there are things the industry just doesn't seem to want you to know.

Michael: You've raised an interesting point. This problem has been going on for years. Elderly people experience it all the time. They are placed in situations that they would not choose to be in if they had the power to make decisions for themselves. And so, too often they are forced into skilled nursing homes; they are pushed into board and care; they are sent home with less than adequate care. They've been disempowered -- just because they're elderly.

Gail: At some point, they have chosen -- as our younger patients have chosen -- not to fully understand what is happening to them. Not accepting the changes, wanting to go back to their healthier selves. And the one I love, "the way it used to be".

Michael: Right! In some respect being in denial can kill you.

Gail: I don't think it's just a matter of killing you.

Being in denial creates a tremendous amount of suffering.

Michael: That's the real truth.

Gail: It's not only physical suffering, but it's emotional suffering. Because the assumption is "I'm going to be taken care of. The medical industry is going to help me. And helping me means that they're going to supervise all levels of my care. When I'm terminally ill, they will tell me how long I have to live. They will keep me pain-free. They will tell me all the things I need to know so that I can have good quality of life."

Michael: That is the assumption.

Gail: And the healthcare industry has done nothing, absolutely nothing, in the last 50 plus years to change that assumption. We hear a lot of horror stories. And while people can often point their finger to a particular culprit, the problem is in fact industry-wide. This is not about one patient and one doctor, or one doctor and one type of clinic or insurance company. It's across the board. A lot of people are horrified when they get to the end stage of their illness. Then it's too late. They've waited too long.

Michael: This is very common with Medicare recipients. Elderly people who have been led to believe that at age 65 they would have medical insurance paid for by the government, by their having paid into it all these years. Medical insurance that would take care of them --- take care of the expectations you've just mentioned. However, their high expectations have always been unfounded and unfulfilled.

Gail: Right! Just as most people don't understand their health insurance policy until it is far too late.

Michael: When people go to buy or choose an insurance plan, they see in the plan 60 or 100 home health visits. A visit is up to 4 hours. Maybe the plan covers 60 days in a skilled nursing facility. People who are healthy think that's a lot. Here's news for you, that just ain't so! If you're suffering from a terminal disease, you need long-term- care insurance, or you need to have the ability to pay for long-term care, or you need to have the ability to pay for on-going care in the home -- on-going care! Because the safety net people think is out there does not exist. It never did exist!

Gail: Why do we assume that it does exist? What was the mechanism that made people think adequate coverage ever existed? Has there been a change in attitude or has there been a change in care? Has the technology outpaced the insurance company or the Social Security Administration's ability to cope with it?

Michael: Yes. One change is going on. With the advent of managed care, something has begun to be said, but unfortunately, it's too often said after the fact. Managed care is saying to the patient; "Here's what you have available to you. These are things that we can provide you. There are limits. There are boundaries to what we are able to do. There are some things that we probably could negotiate. This pile over here are things we will not cover any longer. You need to have coverage above and beyond what we're able to provide." In some situations, they are saying to patients, "You need to make some decisions about what you want and how you choose to proceed." However, not everybody gets that information. In fact, most don't, and those that do typically respond, "Oh, I'm supposed to choose" or "Oh, I'm supposed to be part of this." They have none of the skills or training to make any decisions.

Gail: How many case managers actually talk to the patient?

Michael: Case managers for insurance companies generally don't get involved with a case until a certain dollar limit is reached. And then they just stop paying for services.

Gail: And prior to that there may be no communication. By the time a patient is end-stage and the bills have finally mounted up to where the insurance company has taken a serious look, that patient quite often is no longer capable of making decisions. They're not capable of participating.

Michael: Those are the horror stories that we are all used to hearing.

Gail: What can we tell people that they need to do for themselves in advance? Do they need to demand that their insurance company provide a case manager?

Michael: They need to do exactly that. They need to request case management. Requesting a case manager is something they have a right to do within most insurance plans.

Gail: This information is critical. This is what you have to do when you find out that you have a long-term illness. You need to demand that a case manager be provided, and the insurance company has to comply.

Michael: Actually, it's in their best interest to comply. Because having a case manager doesn't necessarily give you the right to say, "I want everything."

Gail: I certainly understand that.

Michael: Having a case manager will give you someone who will advocate for you and discuss with you what your options are -- from the insurance standpoint.

Gail: You made a very good point when you said that the case manager lays out the exact dollar amount, the areas they're willing to negotiate, and the areas they absolutely will not touch.

Michael: Right!

Gail: As a patient, you need to understand where your insurance company is coming from in relationship to your treatment.

Michael: Absolutely!

Gail: What kind of options do you have with Medicare and Medicaid programs? Do you have the same options? Is there a case manager involved at some level?

Michael: Generally, facilities or programs providing care have case management as a component of their service.

Gail: That's case management. At what point does the physician have the responsibility to start putting into place those things necessary for your care? Whether it's a medical intervention, a personal conversation, or simply calling the family.

Michael: Physicians usually make assumptions that things are being done. It's rare that questions are asked by the physician of the patient, like "Do you have anyone you can talk to about this kind of stuff? Do you know what all of your options are in terms of home care? Do you know what services are available to you?" Hopefully, the physician will have a good assistant who will be able to give you the requested information, but, remember, you will always have to ask.

Gail: The point is that no one wants to take responsibility, and the patient just doesn't know to ask. They don't know if it's appropriate. They don't even know if they'll be listened to. Maybe they've tried at some time during their treatment to have a discussion with their physician, and the physician has turned away. And they figure, "I'm not supposed to talk about that." And they stuff it!

Michael: The problem goes way back to the physician's training.

Gail: We have to go back to the physician because the physician is the engineer. The physician drives the train. The way the system now works, the physician doesn't get paid for making telephone calls; they only get paid for seeing you in an appointment setting, or if treating you in some manner. There is no added incentive to pick up the phone and make a call on your behalf. That may change.

Michael: Although there are some physicians who will do that.

Gail: I understand that. But there is no incentive for the majority! There is the possibility this may change with insurance and government enlightenment sometime soon.

Michael: Exactly! And with a managed care environment there should be some other mechanism in place. There should be someone who steps in because in a managed care environment the physician is not in control.

Gail: Let's say you're in a managed care environment and you have CHF, a progressive, terminal disease in which you go from having a heart attack to needing a heart transplant. You're terminally ill. You have been assigned a specialist that treats CHF, and that physician says, "You are now a transplant patient." At that point you would think someone would start preparing the patient for what's going to follow.

Michael: You would assume. But we know that generally no one does. The important thing is that something happens between just being diagnosed and then getting a poor prognosis. Something occurs! There's a change that goes on within the body, there's a change in the language that we use, and there's a change in the level of intensity of treatment.

Gail: And you will be given a new doctor, a super specialist. But nobody's driving the system. The system is just kind of cruising along. And squeaky wheels get greased. If you're a squeaky wheel with demands for honest, informed conversation, you'll get a different level of attention. You'll get someone to grease your wheels and get them on the right track, hopefully. Someone is needed to help you deal with a very confusing, frightening trip. And you will need to be the one to initiate that conversation.

Michael: I want to take the doctors off the hook a little. For one thing, I don't think that they can finesse that critical conversation.

Gail: I don't think most of them have the training, aptitude, or motivation to finesse that conversation. And everything is telling them it's not in their job description.

Michael: Then that physician needs to understand that there are people in the community who will gladly help as long as the physician is willing to relinquish some of the control.

Hidden Agendas -- Medical

Gail: Let's talk about the hidden agendas of doctors, hospitals, and healthcare providers.

Michael: Medical students are subtly taught that death is the enemy. It's been said that "Disease is a riddle seeking a solution." Solving the riddle becomes the focus of medical intervention. We have made solving the riddle into the various specialty fields -- oncology, cardiology, infectious disease -- all special ties attempting to solve their respective riddle -- cancer, heart disease. What if your riddle cannot be solved by your riddle specialist? Will you be enjoined into pursuing the riddle at all costs? Even if it kills you? At least we are gaining new information that might solve it the next time. Well, so you are told!

Gail: But that's not going to include you. You're going to die!

Michael: Sometimes that is the agenda that's put out there. "Well, you know, at least she did this treatment so that others will maybe gain some information from this in the future." If you're the patient, you have the right to say "baloney" to that. You're not a guinea pig -- unless you choose to be one. Unless it's important in your life to help them to gain information about your disease. If that treatment is going to cause you suffering, is it worth it? That's a conversation you should have with yourself.

Gail: Before you have that conversation, you've got to have a very clear understanding of what that suffering is going to be, and that's what they won't tell you. That's their hidden agenda. What they're going to say to you is, "Oh, you'll be a little nauseous, or your hair might fall out, or you'll have mild flu-like symptoms but there are all kinds of ways to control that." The fact is that the physician won't be there to hold your head as you wretch for 15 hours into the toilet. The nurse may or may not show up when you want them to treat you with whatever pain relief or nauseous relief the physician has prescribed, but you might end up having to wait 15 to 20 hours, or over a weekend, to get relief from your "mild symptoms." The only way you can know what those symptoms are going to be like is to speak to someone who has gone through the treatment themselves, and you will find those people in a disease specific support group. Then you really have to look at what their health situation was at the time versus what your health situation is at the moment.

Michael: The bottom line is if something is presented to you that's experimental or that's going to further the research into your disease, then you should ask questions. Don't go blindly into it. Don't be guilted into it, either. Find out as much as you can about that particular treatment.

Gail: The exception would be a study in which you are one of the first to participate. That is a decision that you as the patient have to make without information because there would be none available.

Michael: And that may be helpful to you. You may feel comfort in knowing that you are furthering the research into your disease. But we don't want you to go into that type of treatment quietly.

Gail: Kick and scream. Raise your voice -- and remember, you have the right to say "No!" and to say "Stop!" at any point.

Michael: Although this book may be titled "Dying 101," it's really about living and how you choose to live the time that you have left. It's important to have these options explained to you so that you can use whatever time is remaining to be honest, to be open, to be direct, and to deal with your life as you choose.

Gail: Remember, the medical community's agenda is to get you to do the treatment -- period! If you don't, they may want very little to do with you.

Hidden Agendas -- Family

Michael: We've talked about a lot of hidden agendas. But what about hidden agendas in relation to the family?

Gail: The family's hidden agenda is to keep you alive. To stop your dying. To force you to go back to normal -- whatever they perceive normal to be. Although the hidden agenda appears to be the same, each member of the family is going to act out in a different way to get something different out of you.

Michael: Okay. I'm going to be the "devil's advocate," Gail. What's bad about the family having a hidden agenda of wanting you to stay alive?

Gail: It isn't bad. And in the early stages of the disease, it's extremely important because they're your rallying point. They're the ones that are fighting for you in ways that you can not fight for yourself. And in the beginning, a lot of patients have gone into remission and remained in remission for years and years because of the family or a loved one's ability to fight the fight for them.

Michael: As well as to obtain information for them and to do all sorts of other things.

Gail: Yes, because in the early stages of any disease, the loved one in your life, or those family members and friends that are there, can make the difference in whether or not you have an early death or a later death. However, for the late-stage, end-stage patients, that same drive, that same longing, that same agenda can be destructive.

Michael: At some point, you are ready to let go. You're ready to move into the next phase of your disease, and your family and friends do not move with you.

Gail: Exactly.

Michael: You have to force that movement because in some respects their desire for you to live may actually cause you to suffer because they're not allowing you to get other information that may keep you from suffering.

Gail: And they also may stop you from speaking your truth at a time when it is extremely important for you to speak your truth. Your life is ending, and there are things that you need to say. One of the things that occurred to me during one of our grief-recovery groups was that you, the patient, do your grieving prior to your death. The family is not allowed to grieve until after your death. In fact, for a period of time, you and the family are in conflict. You have a need to discuss honestly where you are -- "I'm dying: I'm uncomfortable; I'm in pain, I'm finishing up; I want to tell you goodbye." The family doesn't want to hear that, the family will do anything to shut you up. And if it becomes too intense for you, you will seek other people to talk to. You will find the walk-ins; you will find the therapist; you will find the best friend.

Michael: You and the person whom you select may start alienating the family.

Gail: Yes, and at that point, the family becomes angry, hurt, jealous, and they start acting out against you and the person that you've chosen to have as a confidant. As you know, we've seen it time and again. Everything from the mother who flew out here and broke into her son's apartment to steal his valuables because there was a problem with the lover. All the way to children returning to infantile behavior to get attention back from the parent. We've seen it all.

Michael: By the way, when you do shift gears as you move another step, you have to let people know you've shifted.

Gail: Don't be in too much of a hurry for your

family to follow you. In other words, give your family an opportunity to slowly move with you. Don't demand that they move with you on your time schedule.

Michael: Remember that you may be just testing this information out; you could be wrong.

Gail: Yes, you could be wrong. But most of the time you'll have that subconscious knowing, and you'll probably be right.

Michael: Most of the time.

Gail: You've reached the point in your disease where there is a "subconscious knowing." It seems that, for the most part, we take 9 months to come into this world and, in the case of final decline in terminal illness or old age, 9 months to go out of it. And if you look back on a dying patient, you will see that at some time around the 8th or 9th month prior to their death, they will start doing things in a different way. Their conversation becomes different. Their posture, their facial expressions, their reactions, and all sorts of things start to change. And when you're in conversation with them -- again this is hindsight -- you realize they were saying goodbye to you. That every conversation you had with them was closure. It was not opening up new doors; it was not talking about future stuff. It was closure. Even when people drop dead suddenly, their family often see some of this when they revisit the last year of their loved one's life. It's amazing how often a stranger, or a business associate, or someone you didn't think was that close to the patient will come forward and share a conversation they had with the patient two weeks before they died. Conversation that was relevant to the family. In group, we know when that shift occurs, and we know when it's time to start saying goodbye to them. They tell us.

Message 4: Practicing

Medicine – When they get it right, they will let you know.

Gail: The practice of medicine involves levels of just that – practicing. Being proactive regardless of the circumstances. The idea of not treating an illness just isn't a part of the medical community's thinking. Therefore, it's a misguided expectation for the patient to think that at some point the physician is going to say, "We can't go any further with this."

Michael: It's making unrealistic assumptions about your physician's power.

Gail: And about the type and amount of information that the physician is willing to share with you. The assumption from the patient's standpoint is "You, the doctor, are an adult; I can speak to you and you can speak to me adult-to-adult." The fact of the matter is the physician will never say, "No more" I remember "A". At the end, the physicians were continuing to treat her in an aggressive manner but were not addressing her immediate problem, which was the infection in her foot. It was almost as if the foot didn't exist. Since they couldn't do anything about it, they wouldn't discuss it. They only wanted to discuss what they called "positive things" - this experimental treatment and that experimental treatment.

Michael: "These are things that we can do -- so we'll deal with what we can do and ignore what we can't do."

Gail: And the lack of acknowledgement -- the silence on the part of the physicians -- that alone was driving "A" crazy and causing great pain, anxiety, and stress. Finally, "A" and her husband found the vocabulary, the language, and the assertiveness to say, "What about the foot?" "What about the cancer?" "And what about the pain?" The physicians didn't know what to do. The physicians froze. No suggestions were made by the physicians about how to relieve the suffering. Never once! Yet the patient assumes that the physician is going to say: "There is nothing more we can do about your foot." "We need to put our efforts towards minimizing your pain."

Michael: This is what the patient expects, but this is not what the patient is going to get.

Gail: It hasn't always been this way.

Michael: That's true. As I mentioned earlier, physicians had very little technology at their disposal in years past. They had to observe. They had to sit with the patient. They had to ask questions. That was their training. Today we are very dependent on technology for healthcare. We slide you in, or connect you to, machinery, and we can see what's going on inside your body. Or we perform tests by taking out a piece of your body or a fluid. We can tell what's going on without even meeting you.

Gail: But relying on technology misses the point. The point being that what you think is going on in your body is more important to you than what some test says.

Michael: Because you may be saying, "I feel like life is slipping away from me." Or "I'm tired. I just don't have the energy to do this any more." That's different from the test saying, "I can pinpoint exactly what the problem is, and this is something we need to do." "We need to cut this out or we need to remove that. "When you tell your doctor what's going on, they include that information in their practice on you.

Gail: And the physician is never going to give up practicing on you. Each of us is an individual, and, therefore, each situation is truly an experiment.

Michael: Each case is a way of practicing for the next case -- even if each situation, each individual, is unique.

Gail: What effects does practicing have on the family?

Michael: Many families wish they had been given more information. For example, research has been gathered on families whose loved one went through a hospice program. One of the things these families routinely have said is that they wished they had known sooner about the available options. They wished they had known sooner that they could have chosen a different approach.

Gail: Were these the people who ended up as primary caregivers?

Michael: Yes, these were the family members and partners.

Gail: Quite often the family does not know how sick there loved one is until suddenly they're in the hospital having a 10-minute conversation with a physician. Until then, there may have been no involvement between the family and the physician.

Michael: Yes, even though at this time there generally is at least someone who is aware. It is a rare patient who keeps his or her family completely in the dark until almost the end. It's not common but it is rare.

Gail: Also, there is a tremendous difference if you're married or single and if you're gay or heterosexual. If you've been very private, you quite often don't pull the family in.

Michael: And, generally, the physician's involvement is still only with the patient. Family members are still depending on the patient for information. "How was your doctor's appointment, dear?"

Gail: At some point -- depending upon the disease -- the patient loses control. And the family members enter the picture and are introduced to the physician. And the physician has 10 minutes to spend with the family to get across the diagnosis and condition of the patient. The family members are then saying, "You're not getting the right info. Because if we had known the options, we would...."

Michael: The family expects the healthcare community to give them the options.

Gail: Specifically, the physician.

Michael: Yes, everybody waits for the physician to give that information.

Gail: Not understanding that the physician doesn't want to be in that position. The responsibility has been thrown on him or her, and they don't want it!

Michael: That's right.

Gail: So, when you are lying at home or in a hospital and the family suddenly realizes, "We've got a situation here." What happens? Is the physician going to help?

Michael: Someone within the family, either the patient or a family member, has to bring it up. It could be a spouse. It could be an adult child. It could be a sibling. It could be a non-relative who holds the Durable Power of Attorney. Someone has to stand up and say, "We need something else here. We need a different approach." Whose body is it? Whose death is it?

Gail: The patient's.

Michael: Not in the end.

Gail: Yes, not at the end. But in the beginning the patient is in charge. The patient is going to have to direct traffic. Again, we keep getting back to responsibility. The patient has to set certain things up. If not, the family may show up, and the physician may say, "I ain't got time for this, honey." He's not going to say it that way, but that's how it will be heard. He's going to tap dance, and tell you how busy he is, and get off the hook. And the family members are standing in the hall saying, "What do we do?" Who will help them? How about the social worker at the hospital?

Michael: Yes, that may happen. But I am a social worker, and I don't think that usually occurs. Most social workers are not completely comfortable presenting difficult information to patient and family. Certainly not until after the physician has spoken to them.

Gail: So here you are -- a patient with a terminal disease. You already know that you're pretty sick, and you have a whole bunch of people around you who are projecting their own fears about death and dying on you. "Oh, my G-d, I can't possibly tell him that information. It's like I'm looking in a mirror, and he probably feels the same way I do. And I'd be scared!"

Michael: As you and I know all too well, the real problem at end-stage is that the patient is not in charge. It's all those other people. Control is in the hands of the family, or other surrogates, then the physician, and then the insurance case manager. Maybe several other healthcare providers. Eventually, the patient fits in there somewhere. That is if they want to. Or if they can.

Gail: That's quite a list!

Michael: If you're the patient and you want any

control, you need to speak up -- way back at the initial diagnosis or in the middle while you're sustaining treatment. If you wait until the very end, other people are going to make decisions about what happens to you. And they may not necessarily be the decisions that you would choose. Everyone is going to pull the family aside and say, "What do you think he'd want?"

Gail: And the family is going to stand there with egg on their faces.

Michael: They're going to say, "We never asked". Or when things get really bad, "Well, honey, you're really bad now." They have to guess what you would have done. People miss opportunities to provide or share information for fear of causing it to occur. They don't want to talk about death because they're afraid that will make death happen. Or that if we made plans about what happens during the dying, then that means it's really happening. It brings reality into the room. And no one wants to deal with this reality because it's too uncomfortable.

Gail: Except if you are the patient, and you are lying there suffering -- that's the reality. You are going to take the brunt of your own indecision and the indecisiveness of the family. And, in some cases, you're going to set it up that way. You may be so shame-based that you, in fact, believe that the suffering is justified. You may not take any action on your own behalf; you may then die in agony because you feel that you deserve it. So, if we look at the pecking order of who's in charge, how could we reverse it for the optimal effect?

Michael: By understanding what's going on and practicing different ways of dealing with it. We're going to offer a list of things that you can practice. You're going to practice in two ways. You're going to have an emotional practice and a physical practice. And you're going to get input back from your family members. It's very important for everyone involved to understand the points made in the list.

Gail: Let's begin.

Practice Grieving

Michael: As you begin to practice dying, you will be practicing the grieving of your losses -- of what was and of what might have been.

Gail: O.K. You're going to grieve lost opportunities. You're going to grieve missed chances. "I didn't finish my degree." "I didn't marry." "I didn't have children." That's going to be a part of your grieving, as well as other losses. Loss of role, loss of position, loss of possessions, loss of relationships. All significant losses!

Michael: You are feeling grief for the things that are falling away. The losses will continue to come up -- particularly in the early stages.

Gail: Then you'll learn to expect them -- learn to appreciate them, embrace them, love them, cry over them, forgive yourself, and let them go. Of course, you're not going to be able to totally let them go. Grief will keep popping up periodically. But the more you deal with it, the less painful it can be.

Practice Withdrawing

Michael: Then you begin to practice withdrawing -- pulling away.

Gail: And the first people you practice with are generally the people on the fringes of your life.

Michael: This is the supporting cast.

Gail: Exactly. And the supporting cast may be business associates. They may be acquaintances you periodically have dinner with. They may be people from different organizations that you see three or four times a year. These are not the main players in your life, so you practice withdrawing from them first. And you may find that during your practice, you're getting angry, and you're using anger to push them away. Or maybe you're making them mad so that you can leave. People get very confused as to why they're being pushed aside. "Well, he never acted that way towards me before." Or "She was always a kind and loving and patient." All of a sudden, you've turned into a raging maniac. This is a way of withdrawing. A type of practice.

Michael: Withdrawing can also mean detaching. It's important to allow the withdrawal because people who are dying don't have the time or the energy to deal with the details. The supporting cast gets dropped quickly.

Gail: Very quickly! Generally, they get dropped even before your job is dropped. If you're still capable of working, you'll want to find ways to preserve the essential parts of a normal life style. So, your first withdrawal is from your supporting cast. Then you move your practicing in a little closer, and you begin to practice with some key players. It may be your immediate boss. It may be a brother that you're close to. It may be the nurse in the office of the doctor you've been seeing for a while.

Michael: People who are dying need to realize that they do have a job. You are still employed, but you are employed by yourself. The pay is poor, and there are no fringe benefits. But you still have to work for yourself. And what you're doing by getting rid of those layers of people is focusing your energy on what's important.

Gail: Excellent! A lot of you will relate to this because you already do think of yourself as "a job."

Michael: You should not blame yourself for not working or feeling like you're not contributing -- because you are. You're contributing to your own well-being, you are conserving your energy, and you're providing yourself with the ability to have quality of life.

Gail: If you are a friend or family member, this is why you shouldn't take it personally if someone is withdrawing from you.

Michael: Yes, if you are a friend or family member and need to address this, deal with it in your support group or with someone, other than the patient, who is your support. You can send the patient a letter. You can send them a card. You can do some nice things for them over the phone, but don't expect them to call you or ask to see you.

Gail: And that can hurt a lot. Especially if you are emotionally attached to someone and find that you are on the fringes of their life -- not one of the main players. That is very hard!

Michael: That doesn't necessarily make you less important. You were part of that person's life. But now they have only so much energy to use, and they must use it in the most efficient way possible. And if you are not a front line, key player, you are not useful to them. You are going to suck energy from them that they could be using to -- read this book, to listen to some music, to write a letter, to make phone calls, to play with their dog -- or whatever. Don't feel bad if they haven't included you in that. The most helpful, loving thing you can do is to honor their need to conserve energy.

Gail: Remember, dying is very private, and we are intruding.

Michael: Right. We are intruding.

Practice Becoming Angry

Gail: Anger plays a very important role because it can give you both the strength and the clarity to do what you need to do for yourself. Anger takes a lot of forms; it isn't necessarily raging at others. It can be internal anger -- at yourself.

Michael: And it can clarify who is really your

friend and who is really going to be there with you through it all. Although you're not angry with that individual, you may use their name and scream at them. But that's not the problem. The problem is that you're angry! You're dying! They get to stay; you have to leave. You have the right to be angry about that.

Gail: And if you're a participant in the life of a dying person, you have to be willing to take their anger. If you're going to be a key player in a dying person's life, the anger is going to be a part of it.

Practice Playing Normal

Michael: Sometimes you just want to get away from it all and "play normal."

Gail: Yes, that's when you go out into the world for a couple of hours, or half a day, or maybe even a whole weekend -- depending on your physical abilities -- and you play like you're normal. You do all the things that you've done before, and it feels wonderful. When it's all over, you return home and you have a good cry. Your family members are looking at you like, "What do you mean? You just did this all weekend long. Why can't you do it now?" The family becomes upset and confused because you just had a good time while they're still suffering. Understand that you're entitled to that. You're entitled to play normal and to do it as often as you can. Hold court. have a glass of your favorite wine, maybe go sit in the yard, touch your favorite plant -- whatever. Play at being normal for periods of time. That is a great way to practice.

Practice Making Difficult Decisions

Michael: When you find you're having difficulty making decisions, you get an understanding of how difficult it is to be a physician and practice medicine. Because there's always a series of choices or series of decisions to be made. Any one of them could be the wrong one. But this is not a wrong one. It is the choice you made. It is the direction you took. You can't turn back. You're going to make some choices that may not be so good and some others that will be good, but in any case, they'll just be choices. Realize that having a difficult time making decisions really slows you down. It paralyzes you. If you understand that the choices you make are simply the choices you make, then you can move forward. As Fritz Perls, the famous psychiatrist, said, "A mistake is just another way of doing something."

Gail: Making decisions is a form of practicing. For example, I remember when my friend "F" called me up and said, "I've made the decision that I want to die." The next three times that we talked, he told me all the reasons why he wanted to live. But the fact is, he had already decided to die. Even if his message to the outside world was that he had changed his mind.

Michael: There is a tendency on the part of you, the patient, to appear as though you've changed your mind. Others have to listen very carefully. Because sometimes you may make a decision but won't tell everyone about it.

Gail: Or you can't hold it. The fear may be too great. What you may do is say, "Well, I've decided to do this." And then panic halfway through it and decide "No, No, No!" That's practicing. You may do that two or three times before the decision is actually made.

Michael: My experience has been that when a person makes a decision like that, the words come out of their mouth and hang in the air -- ominously. It's almost as though, "Oh, gosh that felt terrifying and good at the same time."

Gail: As we said, you're putting it out there. You're practicing. You've thought, "Oh, my G-d, I said that?" You let it hang there and then you want to retract it because you may have said it two weeks or a month before it was appropriate. But you need to say it. And people around you need to hear it.

Michael: Also, it helps you find out who is safe.

Gail: Because if you try to discuss it with someone who doesn't want to hear it, that person will run away.

Michael: When you find out that a person doesn't want to hear it, then you can cross that person off your list.

Gail: And hopefully it won't be a primary caregiver -- such as a parent, a spouse, or an offspring.

Practice Talking About Death

Michael: When you are practicing talking about death, it's important for you to realize that the one and only place you may be able to do it is in the confines of a support group or a therapy group -- unless your family members and friends are prepared. They often superstitiously believe that as long as you don't talk about it, it won't oc- cur. Even some group members may have a hard time hearing it.

Gail: I have seen situations where patients are so secure that they are comfortable talking about anything. They allow their family to practice hearing it -- hearing the language over and over again, dealing with their own reactions, and de- fusing their own fears.

Michael: I've seen some patients do that with great success. Making jokes or little comments about dying or being dead can defuse the whole situation. "Dark humor" has value.

Gail: It gets to the point where family members

and friends start making their own jokes, and it seems to work quite well.

Michael: Depending on the personalities involved, that can be a wonderful solution.

Gail: Also, the patient can then practice some of the fantasies that they've had about their own dying and death. We're all a product of TV and movies, and we've all got this image of how we're supposed to die versus how we really do die. The "supposed to" is that I get my family and friends around me. I smell good. I'm on this beautiful bed with my hair done up and my makeup on. And I give an eloquent speech. Then I take my last gasp and leave the Planet, and everyone dabs their eyes. Well, we know that isn't the reality. The reality is often a messy room, unpleasant smells, delirium, or dementia for several days or weeks. And there are no final words.

Michael: And that is why it's important to have meaningful conversations with people while you still can. For example, telling someone how much you care. How much you love them. It's important to do those things while you still can. While you can still hear, while you can still read, and while you can still say "thanks." Because there's going to be a time when nothing can be said.

Gail: And the scene can run the gamut, from being very quiet to being very noisy and emotional -- but always very intense.

Michael: The thing that's important for you to note -- as someone who's going through this -- is that you are tuned to a different frequency than the rest of the Planet. Your radio waves are tuned to a different station on the dial. Only other people who are tuned to that frequency can hear you in the way you intend to be heard.

Gail: That's why it's so important to be around your own kind. And we're not talking culturally or sexually or chronologically. We're talking about being with other people with belly buttons who are dying -- being in a support group. We cannot over-emphasize how important this is.

Michael: And that support group doesn't necessarily have to be a formal group. It can be with some folks that you have gotten very close to who are going through the same thing. Who happen to have lunch or breakfast on a regular basis or who happen to have had special interests prior and are all now going through this. A very important part of practicing is getting used to the idea of not being here.

Practice Making Arrangements

Gail: This has to do with fantasizing and visualizing what you think is going to occur. Even making the funeral arrangements. You may want to talk about who's going to be there, who's going to speak, what kind of flowers, whether or not Aunt Martha is going to have her favorite bottle of sherry. There's no limit on the arrangements that can be made in advance. Even wanting to be buried in your Ferrari or your favorite Volkswagen. It's only a matter of money!

Michael: Speaking of making arrangements, several advance directives need to be made.

Gail: Family members and people around you

are not going to want to hear about these arrangements. They're not going to want to participate in them. Some maybe. Perhaps one or two. But for the most part, they're not going to want to participate. It's going to be a bit overwhelming for them. There, again, we get back to who you can talk to. You have to be selfish enough at some point to say, "I'm going to talk about this stuff. If you don't want to listen to it, I'm sorry, but I have a need to talk about it. And I have to talk about it with you because you are my family. Let's get on with it. Let's start making a list and doing the things we need to do. Then we can talk about other things."

Michael: We'll say more about this in Message 7 -- Important Paperwork.

Practice Going to the Other Side

Gail: It seems we need to practice being on "the other side," which usually frightens the family, healthcare workers, and sometimes the patient. Patients go back and forth, alternating between being on this side for just a few minutes, going over to the other side, and then back again. They "practice" going back and forth. This seems to be a need for everyone, regardless of age and cultural differences, as a way to begin to experience wherever it is they think they're going. You can call it heaven; you can call it astral projection, the twilight zone, purgatory -- it doesn't matter. The time spent there seems to increase as you approach death. Eventually you're spending more time on the other side and less time with the people on this side. At least, this is what has been talked about in group.

Michael: People should understand this and not be afraid if their loved one talks about speaking with people who have died.

Gail: Part of that practice is seeing people who have already died, we are told. People that you loved and loved you.

Michael: Over the years, patients have told me that they had visitors -- people they knew or people they had been close to -- and that the visit had been comforting. It had been a wonderful visit. But they felt like they were going crazy because they knew their visitor was dead. "Why am I seeing dead people?" "Why are they now back in their bodies and talking to me in my room?" "Why are they coming to me in dreams?" If you are a family member, hearing these conversations should alert you that death may be soon. And I'm not saying hours or days or weeks -- but soon.

Gail: There seem to be a lot of fears around this -- for both the patient and the family. What does the family generally do upon hearing this?

Michael: Strangely enough, I've seen most family members feel both fearful and comfortable. It's a little disconcerting. They know what it means; I know what it means; you know what it means. We all have that fantasy that we're going to be carried over.

Gail: Escorted to the other side.

Michael: Whether it's a myth or a fantasy, it happens to a lot of people.

Gail: No matter your religious belief, or whether or not you have one, the same experience seems to be shared. I don't find that people are repeating legends. I find that they are having their own unique experiences. And it is always the person they loved and not necessarily someone who the family or partner wants to hear about.

Michael: I have asked people "Well, was it a nice conversation?" They usually say "Yes." One woman I remember fondly, Mrs. "S", said she didn't want to share that information with anyone because she thought she was hallucinating. She was afraid if she told anyone she was hallucinating, they would put her on medications or they'd think that she was crazy. Before I visited her, I was told that this woman was not lucid, was not in control of her faculties. I asked her about her experiences. I sat and talked with her for 45 minutes and found her to be as clear as a bell. She shared her story with me. This woman was 85.

Gail: Not only the medical community, but also the family, assumed that she was crazy.

Michael: The medical community -- the nurses -- were getting their information from the family, and they were assuming she was not competent to make decisions anymore based on her conversations with her dead father. It was embarrassing for her because prior to that Mrs. "S" had been considered a pretty sharp cookie.

Gail: She was still a sharp cookie.

Michael: Yes, she was. She was just having

friendly visitors.

Gail: There's justifiable reasons for fear. Because the medical community and the family expect you to continue to act "normal" right up until the time you die. Otherwise, you are crazy, or you are demented, or you are delirious -- all of those negative terms that we are afraid of.

Michael: Right. And when they see that, they're going to try to start making decisions for you.

Gail: It should be discussed with the family that this, in fact, is probably going to happen. And the patient should inform key people, "I want to let you know that I will in some way signal you to let you know that I'm still here."

Michael: The important thing is for you to continue to communicate in whatever way works for you -- verbally, or in writing, or even with eye blinks if necessary. If you still have some contact with family members and they can still interact with you, then you should always be consulted before decisions are made. Those decisions should be based on previous conversations and new information that they get whenever they ask you. You shouldn't be kept out of the loop unless that's your wish. And if it is your wish to be unconscious (Option 3 – Assisted Slumber) and not deal with any of this stuff, then make that clear. "You have the right to make decisions for me when I'm incapable or when I'm perceived to be incapable. But as long as I'm able to make my needs known, ask me!" The thing about Mrs. "S" was that her son wanted someone else to ask those questions and to be involved because he realized that he could no longer trust his own judgment about what was going on with his mother. He wanted to have an objective third party go in and say, "Present the information about the program and whether or not she can make a decision about it." I did that, found that she could, and I gave the program my stamp of approval. That took the son off the hook. He would have to participate, but he didn't have to be the one who brought it up.

Gail: So many have told us that, near the end, it's common to have experiences on the other side and to see angels, visions, and friendly visitors. It's shared that generally these experiences will start before you are comfortable sharing it with other family members.

Michael: I'm often told that these things happen around 3 o'clock in the morning when you can't sleep. It may, in fact, bring on those visitors. That may be their signal to come and see you.

Gail: Depending on your life experience, you can have a wonderful show at the end. Those folks on the other side can put on a whole extravaganza for you. If you allow it!

Practice Taking Control

Michael: The whole subject of personal responsibility now really rears its head.

Gail: Yes. Personal responsibility, along with the right language and information so that you can get what you want. It's not a matter of yelling and screaming. Because if you yell and scream and act out inappropriately, they're going to take away your power of control and do things to manage your behavior.

Michael: While it's hard dealing with reality -- the hard, cold facts of having a terminal disease -- you're better off addressing the problems so that you can make whatever time remains more enjoyable. Because being in control really impacts your quality of life.

Gail: It's certainly going to impact your emotional stability. It's going to drive you nuts if you don't have it!

Michael: Because if you think that someone has control over you, you're going to feel helpless. You're only going to be at the whim of the system if you let it happen.

Gail: But if you don't understand what the system is, you don't know what options you really have.

Michael: Right! Who do you ask?

Gail: You start asking the people that have the same disease.

Michael: So, you go to support groups.

Gail: You go to a support group -- that's number 1. Now, I'm finding that most disease-specific support groups, like the Cancer Society, The Wellness Foundation, or the Lupus Foundation are set up to provide information. You have to be a member of that support group long enough to start pulling the meat out of what you're hearing. It may take a while. You can't go into a support group once or twice and get all the information you need. It's definitely impossible.

Michael: Yes! What you're talking about is making a commitment.

Gail: Yes. First, make a commitment to regularly participate in a support group. Try to join early while you are still healthy. Second, make a commitment to attend any organized conferences and lectures that are available through that support group. And third, join the organization that represents whatever disease it is you're dying with. If it's cancer, then you join the American Cancer Society. You find out if these organizations have anything in place that can help you with your social, medical, financial, and emotional needs. Not just to hear lines like: "Think positive and you'll be cured." Or, "Eat the right diet"! "Take the right vitamin."

Michael: Yes, while those organizations may recognize that the disease is terminal, the people who work for those organizations often don't see their patients as dying. Many of those organizations provide some case management. They offer social services so that they can get you on the system. They offer food banks, and they provide limited kinds of nursing.

Gail: Let's get back to the staffing of these organizations and the fact that many of the staff are in denial. Why does the staff not recognize that their clients are terminal?

Michael: Staff personnel are often in denial because they have not dealt with their own fears about death and dying.

Gail: What are the implications of their denial?

Michael: They will withhold information about options because they may not feel comfortable in presenting them. Some of these people may be aware of the options, but they may not feel comfortable talking about them. For example, having worked with hospice and knowing how hospice operates in terms of Medicare/Medicaid benefits, I know that I have to constantly reiterate this information. Too often many staff simply aren't paying attention. So, the information only gets disseminated by the few staff members who are comfortable with it. Granted, they may not always present it accurately. But at least someone's presenting it. They may say, " If you don't go this route, there is hospice that we can provide either in the home or ___." "Wait. I know someone that might be able to talk to you about that."

Gail: The info is basically being thrown away rather than discussed in an open and honest way with the patient. Where do we draw the line? Some staff members come into an organization and they're enthusiastic. It's almost as if they take on the patient or the problems of the patient. Then they go into burnout. Initially, the more enthusiastic or interested, the more weepy or sad they become, the faster they seem to leave. You can generally look at them and tell within a short period of time whether it's going to take 6 months, a year, 18 months, 2 years for this person to finally say, "I've got to get out of here! I can't handle this anymore!"

Michael: So, we have people who are employed to provide services and who may be themselves burned out.

Gail: Unless they've done their own emotional work -- private therapy, support groups, or grief recovery -- and made an adjustment, their pain often puts them in their own state of denial. They're not going to be open and direct with you. Or if they are, they're not going to tell you the whole truth.

Michael: The staff person may not intentionally do that. But they may simply lack the necessary ability to be direct and honest.

Gail: In the meantime, the poor patient is sitting there up to his or her neck in problems and needing help.

Michael: The cases that I tend to get called in on are exactly like that. The phrase that comes to mind is "incomprehensible demoralization." That is the moment when you acknowledge that you never thought it could get this bad -- and it does! It gets even worse!

Gail: No one says, "Sorry! There's nothing more

we can do for you." And the patient is screaming "Help! I need help. Where do I go and who can I talk to?"

Michael: And at the same time the patient is thinking. "There must be something they can do. Maybe they can just slice it off. Put me on the surgical table and slice it off. I'm sure there's new pink skin underneath." But no one tells you that your body can no longer heal itself.

Gail: I remember a conversation I once had with "W". At the end, there was no sense of peace or completion. The ER Doc was forced to tell "W" that he only had a few days to live. His primary physician had been unable to discuss the difficult, final stages with "W". I wish that physician had been able to be honest with him. It was just too hard, I guess, to say, "There's nothing more we can do for you. You're going to die." That part was left for a stranger to do.

Michael: The "nothing" that we can do for you is actually "something."

Gail: Yes! We can do good things when truth comes forward because we're not going to waste your time doing things that are horrible! We're going to let you breathe, let you listen to some music, smell the flowers, and hold someone's hand -- whatever it is that you're capable of doing from here on. Whatever is your choice!

Michael: You were the walk-in for "W". And even though things happened quickly at the end, the process actually started some time ago. He trusted you. You had developed a rapport with him; you had knowledge that you had no problem sharing.

Gail: I met "W" about six months before his death, and what transpired during that short period of time was a building of trust. And you're right! I was a walk-in. I always come from the position of the patient. I don't come from it as the provider. So, I'm dealing from a very intimate place. And I'm willing to acknowledge the fear as long as it is helpful. I'm willing to respect where you are, and all I ask is that you listen to the information and your options. The choice is then yours and yours alone. You are in control.

Message 5: Why Are You Sick?

External and Self-Blame

Gail: We know this is a very difficult and painful message to hear or read about. We hope that we don't do any damage by discussing it, and we also hope that the person who's reading this stays with us long enough to understand our point of view on this subject.

Michael: Almost everyone with a terminal disease, or a life threatening disease, or even an annoying disease, wants to come up with a reason as to why they're sick. For example, you may have been diagnosed with lung cancer or heart disease, and in the past you've smoked. You just know that there's a connection! You've convinced yourself.

Gail: In the beginning, most people think that their cancer is the result of their smoking, or an industrial toxic waste, or some outside force. People look into a variety of causes which remove the blame from themselves and put it on someone or something else. Our anxieties drive our need to find some logic, some reasons for why and how we got the disease. And this gets bound up with our need for a place to put our anger.

Michael: Yes, it seems that there is a need to assign external responsibility.

Gail: Yes. It is called "locus of control," and it's always an external responsibility in the beginning. I know of few people who immediately go into blaming themselves. In most cases, if you've got a very long, protracted disease, you will spend years struggling to figure out why you're really ill. Let's be clear that through most of the disease, you, your family members, and your physician, are going to blame an outside source. Because, in fact, if you find an outside source, you're thinking there's got to be a cure. That's the deception. And for most people, that is a self-deception that they never, ever, ever uncover. This needs to be acknowledged because it's a very honest part of being sick -- blaming something or someone else. Everybody around you is going to buy into it. "I had an accident!" or "Somebody screwed up" or "They didn't give me the right medication" or

"They didn't catch it in time" or They ___ or They ___ or They___. And this can go on for years.

Michael: I'm thinking of other ways that we push off responsibility.

Gail: That's the normal way in which we initially deal with disease. I remember years ago when a patient was talking about her father having died this horrible, horrible death in the hospital, and the constant reference to how the medical community screwed up and how they were going to sue the community -- the doctors, the hospital. the pharmacist. A lot of people go through that. That's a big emotional piece for everyone. And then it seems to subside at some point. There seems to be a letting go and a giving up of that. Because very few people, in fact, do sue. But they all talk about suing; they all talk about shifting the blame.

Michael: A large segment of our culture believes that when something bad happens to us, there has to be some reason why it happened.

Gail: Yes. Our mind has been trained to say, "There's got to be an answer here!"

Michael: People have a hard time accepting either that it was the result of a random occurrence or that it was caused by their behavior. In our need for an answer, we are eventually willing to personally accept the blame.

Gail: Yes, and there are some areas we may want to explore to see if we did play a role. We may have had an emotional experience that was so painful for us that we unconsciously set certain processes in motion. It's not a conscious act. We set up a pattern of behavior for ourselves which then results in our demise. In hindsight, if we're really looking, we can see when the body started reacting to the unbearable emotional stress we imposed upon it. Perhaps we acted out inappropriately. We did too much alcohol; we did recreational drugs; we did sexual behavior that was dangerous; we overate. The extreme of that would be people who cut themselves -- that do violent things to their body. That's a lot more obvious. What we're talking about is a little more subtle -- like the smoker that continues to smoke when they have emphysema. And that comes back to anger -- self-anger, self-disappointment, shame, loss, fear, guilt.

Michael: The reason we get sick might have more to do with "I don't care about me!" or "I lost respect for myself." Something that's a little more intangible.

Gail: Or "I'm bored. I'm defective. I'm unlovable."

Michael: All sorts of behaviors can come from being bored, or all sorts of things can come from a lack of respect for yourself, or a lack of concern for the details of your life. A whole series of events can start to roll when you lose self-respect or lose control of your life. There are very few people who can say, "You know what? I know why I had a heart attack. I wasn't ready to get married. And I could have said, 'I don't want to get married to you!' But I was chicken. I had to have some other event occur to prevent me from getting married." That's what I'm looking for when I ask, "Why are you sick?" "Why are you in this position right now?" And this applies even to catastrophic accidents. Kids that get into a serious accident because there was such trauma going on between the parents that something needed to occur that would bring them together -- or push them apart -- by somehow moving the event forward. Something to relieve the pressure in the family system, perhaps.

Gail: Just change the event. If you feel you're in a toxic situation, you will do anything to get out of it, even become sick. So many times we've all heard, "If you keep doing that, you're going to make yourself sick!"

Michael: The reason we bring this up isn't because we want to blame you for your disease. Quite the contrary. It's because we want you to look for honest reasons why you may be sick, to explore the things that you may be able to do to see yourself clearer and feel better about yourself and about your life. By putting things in perspective, you can live whatever time you have remaining without the guilt.

Guilt and Shame

Gail: Even though you may not be talking about your feelings, on a subconscious level they are there, and you may be acting out the guilt or the hurt.

Michael: You may be causing yourself more pain, more anguish, in a time when your body can't handle it.

Gail: I'm thinking about someone who spoke-up in the late hour at a gathering. He made the statement that he knew the moment his self-esteem became so low that he opened himself up to be infected. Everyone in the room started chiming in on a similar event in their life. They each could acknowledge and reflect on what had occurred for them. Each one of them had a different belief system about what it was that had caused that event. I would say that overall the one thing they had in common seemed to have been shame. What some have actually come to call "toxic shame".

Michael: Deep shame that they didn't feel good about themselves or that people shamed them for being who they are. Or shame because the medical community couldn't help. And they had come to the conclusion it was their fault.

Gail: Exactly! And I can see the same thing occurring with many diseases. We come in with certain genetic weaknesses, and it is becoming more and more apparent to many that our emotions set off those weaknesses.

Mind/Body Interaction

Michael: From my standpoint, the medical community is beginning to come around to that way of thinking. It's beginning to question, "Well, are there physiological reasons for this particular illness in your life right now?"

Gail: Our society in general wants a "quick fix." They want to put a simple bandage on a very complex problem. It's a horrible travesty to shame anyone with a catastrophic illness into thinking that it's their fault or that they can cure themselves. Acknowledging that you may have played a role, forgiving yourself for that possible role, and getting on with your life -- that to me is far more important. By doing good therapy, by being in a support group, maybe by leaving a toxic marriage or relationship -- whatever you feel you need to do to make your life healthier -- you may be able to help extend your life. You're still going to have the same disease follow you around. There's no way to rid yourself of it. It's already in your body. But carrying that horrible shame, guilt, anger, or fear to your grave is such a disservice. One of the things that you and I have heard again and again is that being in a support or therapy group allowed people to talk about their guilt and shame. And by talking about it, they diffused it.

Michael: When talking about it in a support group environment, hopefully no one is going to say, "Oh, you should do this," or "You ought to have done that," or "You could do so and so." No one is going to be critical or try to fix you at that moment, and you are free to release your self-punishment and to forgive yourself.

Gail: Or realize that you don't need forgiving. You didn't do anything wrong in the first place.

Message 6: You Can't Fool the Body

What Is Your Body Saying?
What Are You Telling the Body?
What Are You Seeing?

Gail: Whether you like it or not, your body has a mind of its own. It's on its own path. I couldn't care less what you think you want.Can you climb stairs? Can you eat? Are you hungry? Do you have difficulty breathing? Do you have short-term memory loss? Can you drive? Can you go to the bathroom by yourself? Can you leave the house? Have you stopped participating? Do you want to hide? Are you listening to your body or are you in denial?

Michael: Many people have spent a lifetime not paying attention to aches and pains. They had to numb them; they had to ignore them to be able to function, to go to work, to raise their kids. It's important for people to feel those physical experiences. It's definitely something that you have to learn how to do all over again. Whenever you've got some disease going on. I always tell people to do a "systems check". To go through your body, from head to toe, and listen on another level. It's not something that you're going to physically hear, but you can check your systems by listening for messages and noting what's wrong where. What is going on? Why is it that your body now requires supplemental feeding through an IV? What does that mean for you? Why do you require pain medication on a 4-hour basis? What does it mean? What is your body saying about what's going on?

Gail: Two typical messages are: 1) you are being treated aggressively and 2) you are expected to have shortness of breath and problems with bowels and digestion because of the medication. Until you stop the treatment, you don't really have an opportunity to determine whether or not your body is having a problem functioning on its own. So, at some point, a transition happens. For instance, suppose you've lost tremendous weight and you've got muscle atrophy; someone decides to hook you up to TPN or to a feeding tube. Or suppose it's decided that you simply need liquid food supplements with your regular diet because your body is unable to absorb the necessary calories and you suddenly realize, "Oh, my G-d, I can't eat enough; I have to drink this stuff"

Michael: You have to start listening to those bodily messages. You have to start training yourself to hear them sooner, assessing your system above and beyond the treatment that is being given. You still have to be able to say: "I don't have an appetite." "Why am I not hungry?"

Gail: That's a very good question because the body, having a mind of its own, can decide to shut down.

Michael: There could be any number of reasons why you don't have an appetite. And it's important to say to your doctor: "I don't have an appetite." "I'm not hungry."

Gail: "I don't want to eat anymore." That's a very important message.

Michael: And their response to you when you say that may be, "Well, we can do this for you. You don't have to take food orally. We can supplement you so that it's easier for you to eat."

Gail: Of course, it will only be temporary.

Michael: Right. More often than not, they won't even hear that you're saying, "I have no appetite. I'm not hungry. I don't feel like eating any more." You have to really explore this for yourself. You have to decide. "Am I not hungry because of all these medications, and food just doesn't taste good? Am I nauseous? Am I not hungry because I feel bloated?" Or "I'm drinking lots of fluids just because .... what?". Am I not hungry because I'm dying and this is the end?" Those are difficult questions to ask yourself. Of course, your doctor may not ask you the question because he or she doesn't want to hear you say "No." They want to say, "Well, if you don't have an appetite, we'll give you an appetite enhancer. Or you can try medical marijuana so that you can force yourself to eat." Or "How about if we give you a supplementary feeding." And you do it because it's ordered or because you have a port-a-cath. It's really easy. At 7:30 at night we'll hook you up; we'll unhook you at 7:30 in the morning; and you'll get your food that way. No problem! You get main-lined.

Gail: And they can do that until you die.

Michael: We can do that indefinitely. But the question you may want to ask yourself is "Why am I not hungry?" The only way you can find out the answer is by doing that "systems check". You go through all of your body and find out what's going on. And really hear it! It's only fair that you be aware. There are things your body is going to tell you that you don't want to hear.

Gail: People who are ill complain about the fact that they have no sex drive. "Why don't I have a sex drive?" They don't want to hear that the disease had taken away their sex drive. Especially when they are young. They talk all around the subject. I often point out, "It's very simple. Mother Nature seems to be saying you are 'damaged goods'; She doesn't want you making babies." There are just certain things we cannot avoid. We'd like to be able to avoid them, but we can't. And one of them is that when we get sick, our bodies simply start to close down and our sex drive can be one of the first things to go.

Michael: We live far beyond our usefulness to nature. Once we've raised our children, and they have left the nest, or they are capable of leaving the nest and being self-sufficient, technically speaking, we don't have a biological purpose any more.

Gail: Sexual dysfunction and loss of appetite are two of the ways that mother nature seems to remind us that our bodies have "dwindled". We don't seem to need the sexual drive any more; for most people that seems to be something they can live without. There's conversation around it and maybe some grieving with the loss of it, but it's relatively easy.

Michael: However, there's no way to avoid the loss of appetite. Another reminder that usually follows the loss of appetite is severe bowel problems. You're either constipated or you've got diarrhea

Gail: Those two things seem to occur at the same time. Yet another reminder is that you continue to eat, but you have malabsorption. The food is going in, but it is not getting to your cells. You are still trying to eat three meals a day, but you are getting thinner and thinner and thinner.

Michael: The question you need to ask yourself is "Why is my body not absorbing food?" "Why is that happening?" Those are the kinds of questions you have to ask. "Well, why do you think you're not eating?" Or "Why do you think you're not hungry?" Something is going on, and you are not absorbing food simply because you don't require the same amount of calories you needed when you were an active, healthy person. There's a lot going on, and you need to learn to listen to your body's messages.

Gail: At the same time, you, your physician, and other healthcare providers are going to be giving your body a different message, "More pills, more treatment, more doctor's appointments, more hospitalizations." The physician is going to want to put in the nasal gastric tube. He's going to want to provide some nutritional supplementation.

Michael: Families in this situation feel helpless because they can't seem to do anything for their loved one. Well, you think you can do something; you think you can try to feed them. You make special dinners; you offer snacks; you make sweets. You do all that stuff and force that on your loved one. And that can be a problem for someone who is dying if they're being told, "Oh, you've got to eat! You have to keep up your strength. You've got to eat, eat, eat, eat, eat." Just hearing that message constantly -- when you're not hungry-- is a battle. It's a battle, and I don't think families really understand how much it shames you. Because you can't eat for a reason. You can't eat because you're not hungry!

Gail: What you do is play a game. "Oh, I'm eating! I'm eating three meals a day and snacks." And what you're doing is pushing the food around the plate to get away from that shame. You are constantly being asked, and you lie because you are forced to. Subsequently, you lie to yourself. "Oh, I ate! I ate everything. The "Meals on Wheels" came, and I cleaned my plate and even wanted a pudding." But the reality is that you've only taken a couple of bites.

Michael: Maybe two bites were all you wanted, but you can't survive on two bites.

Gail: And maybe you took the two bites because someone was standing there saying, "You've got to do that." When I ask a significant other if the patient is asking for food, and he or she says "No," then I usually say, "Don't bring it up. If they want something, they'll ask you for it."

Michael: I think that's an important message for the caregiver --whether it's the family or a nurse. If the patient doesn't ask to eat, don't offer it.

Gail: And, as a patient, you need to be very clear about what you are seeing. You may be saying to yourself, "I'm healthy," "I'm not that sick," or "I'm not that far along." "Someone else is really in the mirror." "I can fool them; they won't know how sick I am." But are you seeing the truth?

Michael: What you see in the mirror, for example, is very significant. Taking an honest look in the mirror is hard even for a healthy person. People will often see a pimple and ignore that the rest of the face is blemish-free. But when you're very ill or dying, you may still see the person that was in the mirror when you were well. The truth is difficult because what you see in the mirror is reality. Depending on your illness, you may see someone who has lost their hair. You may see someone whose color has changed. You may see someone who may have more blemishes than they had when they were a teenager. You may see someone who looks almost like a skeleton. And actually seeing those things is frightening.

Gail: Do you stay in denial? Or do you look long and hard, make some decisions, and then set the shock and fear aside?

Michael: It's important to at least pay attention to what's happening to you when you try to make decisions.

Gail: Along those same lines, one of the things we tend to overlook is the reaction of other people. Do they come in the room, bust out crying, and say, "Oh, my G-d, how you've changed!" Do they gasp? Do they weep a little? Do they turn away some possible clues?

Michael: "G" did a presentation with me for hospice. He died maybe two or three months later. He was very skinny. He still had kind of a bloated belly, but his arms and legs were just twigs, and his face was very gaunt. He stood up in front of a hundred people and said, "You know, you couldn't tell that I was sick, could you? You can't always tell when someone has this disease." And my friend who was with me -- she's a nurse

-- looked at me and said, "Oh, my! He's in major denial about what's going on!" He actually looked very ill.

Gail: I remember the comment he made to me much later. It seems he got out of bed to take a shower one day towards the end and said, "I didn't know who was in the mirror." Allow your body to guide you.

So Many Choices

Michael: So much of this puts responsibility on the patient, the least knowledgeable person in the story.

Gail: Yes, what's starting to happen is that the healthcare industry is forcing the patient to participate. Because of the way insurance is structured, you don't just die in a hospital anymore. These days there are a world of things that happen to you between diagnosis and death for which we're unprepared.

Michael: Maybe 70 or more years ago people died at home. Since then, people generally die in a hospital. But the likelihood of your dying at home again is high, if you choose to, if you have a supportive family, if you have supportive friends. It can occur at home, or it can occur in some other setting of your choosing. If you choose to treat aggressively until death, your death may likely occur in a hospital. If you choose to pursue a treatment like hospice, your death could occur in a nursing facility. It could occur in a residential care facility. It could occur at home.

Gail: If you choose aggressive treatment, this is what you're going to find: surgery, chemotherapy, radiation, and experimental drugs and therapy. And for these, you will typically be hospitalized.

Michael: It will be done in a setting where it has to be done -- not necessarily in a setting of your choosing. Some aggressive treatments can be done just about anywhere.

Gail: In the early stages some things can be done at home. But when a patient is end-stage or late-stage and those kinds of things are offered, then the patient has to realize that they are going to need strong support within their home if, in fact, they choose to do this kind of treatment. They can't just go into the hospital because the insurance is not necessarily going to let them.

Michael: The length of stay may be different. They may say that the kind of care you need does not require a hospital. So if you can't be there and you can't be at home, then they'll suggest that you look at a skilled nursing facility or sub-acute care facility.

Gail: My experience has been that unless the patient asks for that care -- unless they know they need to ask for assistance -- then quite often the physician and the hospital will just send them home. In a current example someone living alone in an advanced stage of disease was sent to the hospital for outpatient radiation and chemotherapy. He got to the point where he could no longer walk, no longer drive, no longer ascend his stairs. Twice he was sent home in a cab. And when the cabby dropped him off at his apartment, he sat at the bottom of the stairs and cried because he couldn't walk up the steps. Now, no one came in his hospital room during all this and said to him. Excuse me! Can you walk? Can you feed yourself? Can you prepare a meal? Can you take a shower? Can you drive? No one stepped in and tried to make the necessary arrangements for him to have care at home.

Michael: But someone did step in.

Gail: Yes, I did -- the second time he was hospitalized. But the fact of the matter is that he would have been sent home again had I not stepped in. Someone would have called him a cab, and he would have gone back to his apartment unescorted and in a worse condition than he had been in two weeks earlier when they hospitalized him.

Michael: It sounds like he was in denial.

Gail: There's a difference between being in denial and knowing what kinds of questions to ask. He didn't know what was available to him. He honestly did not know that there was a system in place for him to access. So, he didn't know to ask for it. He certainly didn't know what to ask for. That's one piece. And, yes, the other piece was the denial he developed because his condition had deteriorated quickly and he didn't know it. He also had been making decisions by himself for most of his life and thought he would die if he let someone help him.

Michael: If you're getting information and you're not acting on it, if you're not finding out what you need to know and when you need to know it, then perhaps you are in denial. What's critical is that you're in a setting that's going to prey upon you because you're saying, "Walk on me." "Of course, I can do this all by myself!" "I'm an independent person." So, you've got to honestly tell them the situation and step up on your own behalf.

Message 7: Important Paperwork

House and Stuff

Gail: People are unaware of the number of documents that they have to think about and to research and, most importantly, do something to get them completed. The document that first comes to most people's minds is a "Will." Who gets what? How is property to be split up? But these days, trusts are extremely critical to avoid probate and the time and costs of a will. In addition, unlike a Will which only takes effect after death, a "Revocable Living Trust" allows the person you designate to handle your affairs if you're unable to do so yourself, for example, because you're injured or ill -- and without having to go to court to have a conservator or guardian appointed to do so. The financial implications and differences are major. Check with an attorney for advice on your situation and explanations.

Michael: The documents related to your wishes

for your medical care are quick and easy and of immediate concern. Get all the paperwork completed as soon as possible!

Gail: Remember, "preventive lawyering" is a lot less expensive, time-consuming, and anxiety-producing than "crisis lawyering." Getting things done now will give you and the people you care about tremendous peace of mind.

Michael: The confusion begins when people think that to go to an attorney they need to be wealthy. To have an estate. To have assets. The fact of the matter is that quite often the average person really doesn't understand what they have. They've never sat down and really added up everything of value that they own, much less actually gone to a lawyer. For some, it's scary and most of us need some help putting together questions.

Gail: So, what we would like to do is to give you an idea of some of the things that you have to be prepared to talk about. The first thing that would probably come up is a Will or a Trust. Simplifying it, the Will generally has to do with "things," which includes your BODY from the moment of your death to your funeral. That said, Your Advanced

Health Care Directive, discussed in a minute, can also state your directions regarding disposition of your body and funeral arrangements.

Michael: And your "stuff."

Gail: "I want my grandchildren to have this." "I want my brother to have that." "I want my sister to do that for me." Of course, you can keep the attitude, if you want, that you're never going to die. The Will is basically "the stuff." If you have children or pets, you're talking about custodial matters.

Advanced Directives:
Durable Power of Attorney for Health Care
(Advanced Health Care Directive);
Durable Power of Attorney for
Asset Management;
Living Will;
Directive to the Physician/
Your POLST Instructions

[Note: We aren't lawyers, and you need to check these legal matters out with your own lawyer to see what fits your situation. Unfortunately, some lawyers may not be pro-active in helping with

*these issues. Consider seeing a lawyer whose spe-
cialty is estate planning.]*

Michael: As a part of "Advance Directives"
we have "Durable Power of Attorney/Advanced
Health Care Directive," "Living Will," and "Directive to Physician/ Your POLST document." Basically, all these documents say: "This is what I
want done if you ask me a question and I am unable to answer." "This is what I want done when
I get to this point." These are the key documents
that speak on your behalf. Don't think you can fill
out a "Durable Power of Attorney" and state what
your wishes are at end-stage. At that point, you
may not be mentally or physically able to do so.

Gail: Yes. And it can be challenged. You may be
surprised by whom.

Michael: And how strongly. You want this to be
irrefutable evidence of what your wishes would
be if you could speak.

Gail: And in today's world, with so many living
with a "significant other" or a "partner" and without marriage, this paperwork is absolutely critical.

Michael: The importance cannot be overstated.

Gail: There is a lot of hesitation and fear around doing this. The people who are the least informed are the most afraid to do it.

Michael: There is also a lot of magical thinking that goes along with the whole subject of dying. In our culture we believe that if we talk about dying -- then we will! If we speak of death -- the person will die!

Gail: We have an attitude that people can read our minds. "I don't have to put it in writing." "I don't have to tell them." "So-and-so is going to know how I feel about this." As we all know, this isn't the case; all too often, it is far from it.

Michael: I'm reminded of a family that was trying to turn off life support systems to allow their daughter to die. They had to search their memories for any conversations in which their daughter might have stated her wishes. It was a difficult, essentially impossible, task. If their daughter had written her wishes down, signed her name, had her signature witnessed, there would have been no question about what her wishes were. It will be much easier if you have a document that says, "I want no feeding tubes." "I want no ventilator." "If the ventilator is started, I give you permission to turn it off." This is the POLST document. These documents have weight in hospitals, in skilled nursing facilities, in residential programs. The thing that people sometimes forget is that once something is started, it's hard to get it stopped. And turning it off doesn't mean that you're going to die right then and there. There's going to be some more dying to do before you're dead.

Gail: The first time I had to fill out a "Durable Power of Attorney," (also known as an Advance Health Care Directive) what I was most aware of was the absence of information. There was no checklist; there was not one piece of paper from the medical community that I could reference to learn the possibilities and the alternatives. In reviewing this stuff, not only did I find out that I didn't really understand it, I couldn't spell the words that were needed.

Michael: And you have far more medical background than most.

Gail: But now we have (POLST) or Physician Orders for Life-Sustaining Treatment. More and more States have their version of this document, and if they don't, find one online from another State, and print it out for reference. There's a lot that you are expected to understand, write down, and discuss without the necessary background or education. Those are scary situations for all of us, and we need all the help we can get. Getting that help requires that you take action now, while you're still able. And, once you've signed your health care planning documents, it's essential that copies be delivered to the doctors, hospitals, etc., where you are regularly treated, and that they're placed in your permanent medical charts. Taking copies with you when you travel is also a good idea.

Michael: Explaining that a person has the right to make decisions about medical treatment is a Federal requirement. Skilled nursing facilities, hospitals, home health agencies are required by law to give you information regarding your rights. It troubles me that this is a very small part of the admission process. It is only a little "check off." "Here, just sign here so that we can go on to something else." That conversation could take hours to be adequate. It takes a lot of time and it's very intimidating. With the POLST it makes it easy. But note that it's a rare physician that will ask for what your wishes are, much less, for your paperwork.

Gail: Preparation of this paperwork comes up more often for our senior citizens. With my mother, it was extremely easy because we had discussed life-long what her wishes were regarding her life and her death. When I had to help my in-laws, I found the circumstances to be totally different. It was impossible to get them to talk about their wishes. They diverted me in every way they possibly could.

Michael: I think we've done a disservice to the public by not providing them with a check list so they can understand what the Durable Power is and how to fill it out. Thankfully, we now have POLST.

Gail: Yes. It's something that needs discussing at length with everyone involved -- family, friends, and physicians. At the very least, it can be difficult if this isn't done. "T", a friend who was recently admitted to the hospital, put my husband and me down on his Advanced Health Care Directive as his healthcare agent. Now granted, we've known the man for over 25 years, but we didn't have any idea of his wishes. And he told them to us the night before his surgery -- too late for any in-depth conversation. That's hardly unusual. In our experience, only a minority of people have indicated their wishes to anyone at all for any situation, much less near their anticipated death.

Durable Power of Attorney

Michael: One of the things we have discussed may need some further clarification. There is the Durable Power of Attorney for Health Care, and there is a separate Durable Power of Attorney for Asset [etc.] Management. A Durable Power of Attorney covers financial matters and assigning someone to act as your legal agent. You don't have to be sick to assign a Power of Attorney. For example, you can give someone Power of Attorney to carry out a real estate transaction for you, or open up a safety deposit box, or some other specific action. That's what you can get under a general Power of Attorney. A Durable Power of Attorney for Health Care (Advanced Health Care Directive) has to do with your medical care -- meaning your body.

Gail: And quite often the same individual will serve for both; you do not necessarily have to select more than one person. There may be circumstances under which you meet with your family and work as a team. One family member may say, "I will be responsible for this piece," and another may say, "I will be responsible for that." When we do a Durable Power of Attorney for Health Care (Advance Health Care Directive), we concentrate only on the physical and the medical.

Michael: However, if you are helping someone you are not married to or not legally related to, then you should also have a Durable Power of Attorney that gives you the right to go in to bank accounts, gives you permission to move money around, or pick up mail, or get into a particular box, etc. Family members may try to "finagle" their way around different organizations that unrelated persons cannot; proper paperwork can make this unnecessary.

Gail: If it isn't legal, they cannot "finagle" their way into a safety deposit box. I'm not talking about walking in with a key and pretending. I'm talking about when you actually have to go in and show documents. Yes, you can perhaps manipulate the landlord or the kids in school for a while. But if you have to do anything legal, then you need documentation.

Michael: Right. You need both documents.

Gail: In regard to that Durable Power of Attorney, it is extremely important for handling mail and the responsibility of the bills. It is critical for having access to the checking account or being a co-signature on the checking account. Note that you have to be an owner and not just a co-signature on all bank accounts. There may be many things you want maintained while you're in your medical emergency or until your death -- plants, pets, access to home, yards, extra keys. The biggest frustration for you and me has been the number of people who are alone. Forty-year-olds with seventy-year-old parents. People who have no spouse or lover. People who insist on maintaining their private residence for far longer than is realistic, requiring family members to fly in at the last moment to try to do something that they didn't want to do in the first place.

Michael: And that creates a lot of problems. For example, sometimes people will come in and try to get the bills caught up. If the person is really dying, do we really want to be spending all their money paying off their bills?

Gail: Not necessarily. If, in fact, the person is dying, maybe it would be better for the cash to be maintained and for those obligations to be put on hold -- either indefinitely or for a period of time. Certainly, on the part of a single person, it might be much easier to let bills accumulate and deal with creditors later. I quite often have to remind people of another related matter. Your parents can assume legal responsibility for you if you are not married or if you have not provided legal documents otherwise assigning responsibility. You may be a forty-year-old male or female who has never married and whose parents may be put back into the same position they were in when you were seventeen. You should understand that. It can become a major problem.

Michael: But the parents don't necessarily have to take their roles back.

Gail: No, they don't, but they will be called. What we're trying to do is encourage you to make sure your affairs are in order.

Michael: Maybe we should suggest you visualize a baseball bat bashing up against the side of you head to get you into action. Or a parent coming in and shaming you because you didn't get this done, and you didn't get that done, and how disgusted they are. "I didn't know my son was living this way."

Gail: Oh, yes! How heartbreaking it is to hear parents say they were disgusted with their son or daughter because of his or her lifestyle. Not realizing that their adult child may have been sick for over 10 years. You know, when you have a life-threatening disease, you don't conduct your life in the same manner as someone who is healthy. You don't have the same goals. You don't have the same interests. You don't have the same energy. In one situation, when that piece of information was finally made clear to the mother -- talk about peeling an onion -- 1 watched all the layers fall off. Because, in fact, she had been shaming and blaming her son, not understanding that he had been dying for 5 years.

Michael: A Living Will and Directive to Physician are two documents that support or back-up what you've written on your Durable Power of Attorney for Health Care (Advanced Health Care Directive). Anything you can add to those documents, like the POLST, is very helpful. The more information you leave behind, the better off the people making decisions for you will be.

Gail: If you've had no conversations with them about your wishes, you've left them to make it up. "What would they really want? I thought I knew them, but we have never really talked about this subject." The Directive to the Physician, the Living Will, the Durable Power of Attorney for Health Care (Advanced Health Care Directive), the Durable Power of Attorney of Attorney for Asset [etc.] Management and the POLST are all more than helpful. They really are necessities.

Financial Matters

Michael: What do you really own? You need to do a financial assessment.

Gail: Your job, your salary, your bonuses, your pension, and your savings. Plus any property or investments. Right?

Michael: Yes, just trying to get a sense of where you stand. If you're putting your affairs in order, this will be something that you will need to do.

Gail: Life Insurance. What kind of life insurance do you have? What kind of disability insurance do you have? So, as important as it is to confer with an estate planning lawyer, it is equally important to confer with a knowledgeable insurance broker. It would be very helpful to those who have to care for you if you were to gather all those documents up and have them easily accessible. They should be appropriately placed so that anyone can find them. And they should be listed with telephone numbers and names of the people to contact. Or, there could be a list that shows that you have contacted the pension fund, or the life insurance fund, or whatever it is. And that you spoke to so-and-so and this was a general outline of what you discussed. So that anyone accessing those documents could be current.

Michael: Do you own a house or a condo? Do you own a retirement or weekend home? Where are the mortgage records? Where are the tax records? Do you have a car? A boat? An RV? An airplane? Where are the documents for those items? Where are the "pink slips"? How long have you owned them? Do you have a second mortgage? Etc. Etc. All this information should be available and as complete as possible.

The Trust

Gail: The other thing we want to talk about here is the trust -- if you have set up a trust. A trust is a legal substitute for yourself that can help you avoid the costly probate of your estate after you die. It is of special benefit if you have substantial worth. Talk to a lawyer. If you're middle-aged, then you may have to consider multiple generations -- the generation before you, your children, and, depending on your age, your children's children. You could actually have four generations involved with the same trust. If you have aging parents that need care and have been looking to you for supplementary support -- either financial or physical -- then it will be necessary to create arrangements for those individuals. The trust would allow you to do that. It's obvious that you need to talk with a lawyer about this. There are some good, helpful information on trusts written for lay people online. If you have young children, then we're back to your Will and the subject of custody and guardianship. And, as was mentioned, if you're dealing with adult children who have children, you are usually dealing with yourself, your older parents, and possibly your children. But it, obviously, can get complicated, and expert, understanding, and sympathetic help are usually required.

Michael: And your intentions need to be clear, just like your Durable Power of Attorney and your Directive to Physician.

Gail: Because the fact of the matter is, you may be medically incapacitated for a long time. Your death may not be imminent, and there may be some financial needs that would impact both the generation older than you and the generation younger.

Michael: These are all things that are difficult for us to do as a society. Doing any of this puts you ahead of the majority of people who are out there. It should be a requirement that we all meet because it is the responsible thing to do. Sadly, most won't. It's going to start becoming more the rule than the exception. Case in point would be what the hospitals are now doing. The hospitals have taken on the responsibility of asking you for your Durable Power or getting you to fill one out at admission. At least there's something in place.

Tangible Items

Michael: And don't forget your tangible Items, such as jewelry, gold, silver, antiques, heirlooms and anything else of value.

Gail: Where are they? Are they in a safety deposit box, or do you maintain them in your home? And if you're going to have other people in your home taking care of you, is it appropriate to have valuables in your home? Would it be better to put them in a safety deposit box or with a family member for safe keeping? Or would they be better passed along now to whoever is going to receive them? And, oh, yes, what about your savings account, and your checking account? Where are they? What are the numbers? What banks do you use? Do you have more than one? Do you have stocks, bonds, commodities, pensions, IRA's? Where is your IRA account? Where is your Social Security information? How long have you paid into Social Security? What is your Social Security number? Have you asked Social Security to send you a document outlining your benefits? Do you have a safety deposit box? What's in it? Is it time to get rid of some of the items that we've just listed? Can you sell it? Can you give it away? Would it be more appropriate to transfer it now instead of waiting?

Michael: This is a reminder that you need to consider seeing an attorney. If you think that you can not afford one, perhaps you might attempt to see an attorney through some charitable organization, a legal aid society, or one who does "pro bono" or free work for those in need. At least to get some assistance in making decisions about transfer of property, putting together wills and trusts, and things like that. If you have a lot of money, you know that you need to go to an attorney. If you don't have a lot, that doesn't mean that you shouldn't go; you may still have questions. And in a one-hour consultation, you may be able to get most of your questions answered.

Gail: Go online, and if you don't have a computer, tablet, or cellphone, most public libraries and stationery stores have all of the available forms. Bookstores have "how to" books available. You could buy a financial planner, which will summarize and outline all the things we've just discussed and will give you a reference point. That being said, preparing your own documents without an attorney's assistance can result in irreparable disasters which fail to accomplish what you want.

Support Systems

Gail: Support Systems is another item on the Itinerary.

Michael: Your support system, or those who provide you help, care, and encouragement may not turn out to be who you think. It could be a family member, a friend, someone from a community agency, and or a walk-in. What are walk-ins?

Gail: Walk-ins are people like you and I. Walk-Ins are people who just "show up."

Michael: Just suddenly appear in your life to help.

Gail: Most of the time walk-ins are generated because you took some action. You put yourself out there and accessed some community organizations that you may not have accessed before, such as your religious group or a disease-specific organization. Most of the people that we are involved with have reached out for some help, and a walk-in has been there for them. A walk-in can simply be someone who is also sick who has a little more information or a little more experience than you do.

Michael: In accessing your support system, you will find some disappointments and some surprises. People you thought would be there often aren't -- and vice versa. You may need to make decisions about who you want involved and who you don't want involved --recognizing that you don't have time for the "B.S." or the negative energy. Be willing to risk being honest, truthful, and direct to find out who your friends are. Don't lie!

Spiritual Needs

Gail: The subject of spiritual needs is clearly an important one when talking about death and dying. It is also very personal and not one just anybody can discuss in a way meaningful for you and your personal beliefs. We do want to raise a few issues for your consideration that are not related to the subject of spirituality itself. For example, were you raised in a particular religious community? Do you have a need for something familiar? Do you have a need to go back to that community? To that church? To that rabbi? To that priest? Or have you moved on to something else?

Michael: What are your family's beliefs versus your own? What is religious versus spiritual?

Gail: Is your family's belief system going to be in conflict with yours?

Michael: What comforts you? It's important to request what comforts you -- not them! This is obviously a very personal issue. It's one that we choose not to discuss here because your beliefs are yours and not for us to comment on. And your spiritual beliefs are more about what will happen after your death than the practical issues of your life that we want to cover here.

Gail: In other words, if you're uncomfortable with the priest that Mom has dragged in the front door, then you've got to be really clear with Mom that you don't want the priest.

Michael: I remember a woman who told me about a friend who had insisted on visiting and calling to check on her. While the friend said she wanted to be a support person, she kept insisting on imposing her own belief system. She said, "I have a friend who's a religious practitioner that wants to come and visit you. They're praying for you every week in hopes that you'll be cured of this dreaded disease, and they want to come over and pray over you." One of the things that I found really sad is that the patient didn't realize that she could say, "Do you know what? I don't appreciate your lack of consideration of my beliefs!" or "I don't want what you have to offer, thank you very much," and she could have sent fiend on her way. It often amazes me to find what people are willing to put up with for fear of offending someone. If someone is doing something to you that you feel is harmful for you -- on any level -- you have the right to say "Stop!" "Whoa!" "Cut it out!"

Gail: Learning to say "No!" is a very important step. Learning to stand up for your own belief system is critical.

Michael: People may think that their new mission in life is to comfort you. They were never comforting to you before, but they feel some need to do so now. If they're draining you more than filling you up, then maybe you need to get rid of them. Truth is, they are usually just trying to make themselves feel better. Otherwise, they'd begin by asking you what you need.

Gail: A good way for you to practice setting boundaries is in a support group. You can learn the language and practice the skill to stay in control, to stay clear, to stay present, and say in as kind a way as possible, "These are my feelings, my belief system, and you are to stop."

Michael: People who are long-term survivors have the ability to say "No!", and they know how to do so without feeling guilty. You can practice on some basic things, like "No, I think I'll stay in today." Or "No, I don't want to do that." "That's not how I choose to spend my time right now." Those are some easy ones. And the big ones are "You know, I'm really tired of your mother coming over to visit me and making pudding for me and forcing me to eat. I'm tired of that. I need for her to stop, and I need you to keep her from coming in." Those are the hard ones. You can start practicing on the easier ones, setting some boundaries and setting some parameters on what you're willing to do with the time you have left. With the knowledge that you have a finite life span. How long is really immaterial. How enjoyable is very much material.

The Long-term Survivor

Gail: If you have been taking good care of yourself and been lucky, you may find yourself with a strange problem -- living longer than you planned. Part of your itinerary could easily be, "Well, I'm going to be dead in 30 days." And you may not be! You may stay in your limited condition for a long period of time. Learning to adjust to a long-term debilitating disease is going to take special skills. A support group can significantly help you learn such skills. Because it can be a big shock when you don't die! And one of the things that comes up is the anger around not dying. Having all your ducks lined up, having done your goodbyes, having made your peace, having gotten your affairs in order and then you come to realize you're still alive and being really angry. This cycle creates another set of problems for your caregivers and the people who hold your Durable Power. But more importantly, it creates another set of problems for you, the patient.

Michael: You may get a paradoxical response from people who love you but who are also upset that you're still here. "You know, dammit, I was ready for you to die."

Gail: "And you didn't! You're still alive!"

Michael: "And how do I re-adjust my life to having you here when I had finally adjusted to the idea of your being gone. I was ready and willing to let you go. I loved you and blessed you and sent you on your way. And you're still here!" "Not only are you here, but now I'm having to make decisions to allow you to come back into our home and disrupt me even further."

Gail: This is a time when the walk-ins that we mentioned earlier become very important. Because they will understand the problem and turn their attention to supporting the family members.

Michael: Sometimes you may have to get away from the family -- to take a break. It may be difficult for all of you to be together, too close, for too long, under such intense circumstances.

Gail: Then comes the time when you may need to consider going into a facility instead of staying at home where your needs may have grown too great for your loved ones.

Michael: That is a horribly difficult decision to make because it's filled with significant implications.

Gail: You'll know when to make it. You'll make it when you wake up one morning and you realize that you've changed, that you've adjusted to this long-term disability, and that your family members haven't. The hard part is being able to say, "I love you." "We need to make other arrangements so that you can live a normal life. I'm not going to get better. My situation is never going to change. I'm going to deteriorate further and die, but, in the meantime, you are being cheated out of a normal, healthy life. And I have made the decision to take myself out of this environment so that you can have some normality." People know when this is true, even though they usually can't verbalize it. It's very difficult to give it words because the caregiver feels that they're not loved or that they've done something wrong and bad when, in fact, it's just that the patient has made the adjustment and the family or friend has not.

Final Plans

Michael: There is little that is more difficult than making funeral plans -- making the necessary arrangements for your ending. You may be amazed by how hard it may be for you and others to initiate or participate in this.

Gail: It's another example of the need to assert yourself and to take control.

Michael: Yes. For example, if you have a desire to be cremated, there is a form that you can fill out. It's called an Authorization to Self-Cremate. If you complete that, no one in your family can go against your wishes -- as long as the person who's handling your affairs follows your wishes.

Gail: When you make your arrangements with the funeral home, they will give you that form, and all you need to do is give the completed form back to them.

Michael: Yes. When you make your plans with a mortuary or a cremation society, they will help you fill out all the documentation well ahead of time and make your plans as detailed as you wish.

If you want to orchestrate your death -- that is, your funeral or memorial and the disposition of your remains -- you can! You can have as much control as you choose to have. Some people want to have a lot of control; others want someone else to do it because it's just too difficult for them.

Gail: If you choose not to do it for yourself, then you can authorize someone else to do it.

Michael: Remember that if you die without any plans, the closest legal family member can make whatever arrangements they want.

Gail: We're back to the Will. This document can be used for your body and your funeral arrangements. Note that Wills usually don't mention how your body and your funeral arrangements are to be handled. Things would be much simpler if you include them in your Will or complete them with a funeral home. If you don't and you die, the next thing that happens is someone comes in and fights over your body and the arrangements. This can happen if you give a non-related person your Durable Power of Attorney for Health Care (Advanced Health Care Directive), and you still have a legal family member involved. You die. The person holding the Durable Power of Attorney thinks that they've got authority over your body -- and they don't! It's one of the reasons you really need to contact a mortuary, funeral home, or cremation society in advance. You need to start putting your plans in place. And yes, it is a hard thing to do. But it can be wonderfully freeing to have that out of the way.

Michael: And superstitions aside, you don't die after having just made funeral arrangements. In fact, you do go on to live a little more freely. You don't have to worry about things like whether or not your sister in some other state is going to be opposed to your being cremated -- if that's what your wish is and if you've already signed the document to be cremated, you'll be cremated.

Gail: You want to ask yourself, "Do I care? Is my funeral important to me, or would I rather not know about it and just let people do what they want and need?" If your family follows a specific belief system, are you O.K. letting them do things in their traditional way?

Michael: Or do you have some specific request?

Gail: Does it really make any difference to you? Or are you more concerned about meeting the wishes and needs of other people?

Michael: If you have made the decision not to be involved, it would be helpful to let people know that you don't care, speak up about what you want. Not caring about it carries no judgment! It just isn't important to you.

Gail: Be as detailed as you like - who, what, when, how long, music, food, decor, gifts, etc. Talk with your friends, family, minister, funeral directors, and get some ideas about your options. We'll talk about some ideas in a minute. It's your call. You can be both the director and the central player in the final scene.

Message 8: What Is Left Behind?

Closure.
Damage Control.
Farewell or Goodbye Party.
Final Scenes.
Memories, Memorials, Funerals, and Stuff.

Michael: "Closure" is about unfinished business with family and friends. If you've taken care of everything else, hopefully you have also made a list of people that you need to say goodbye to, or that you need to make peace with, or that you need to be with. That's what "0"- is doing. He's finishing up with some people by going to lunch with them, or having dinner with them, or talking with them on the phone, or allowing them into his space at this time. He's doing things that are helpful to smoothing out the path to his exit from the planet.

Gail: You can do that in a variety of ways. You can ask people to come to wherever you are. You can do this over the telephone. You can write letters

-- letters in advance of your dying or letters to be opened up after you've died. But I think no, I'll do it in person. Because I know closure is extremely important. It certainly is a gift to those you will leave behind, and it can help keep you in a state of good mental health. I don't mean that closure is all sweetness and light and good things. It can be a discussion of the hurts that have existed. Closure should be very direct and very straight forward so people are clear about how you feel and how they feel.

Michael: Another issue in terms of "Closure" is "Damage Control." Making amends and keeping your side of the street clean. I think that some people want to leave the Planet with a clear conscience, and that's actually what that statement means. The cleaning up of old stuff so that you can move forward peacefully. Your soul is not going to be troubled -- and that doesn't mean after you're dead -- but that the time you have remaining is not troubling to you. Cleaning up things that you have done or said or felt about people is helpful.

Gail: For most people there is a scene somewhere in their mind as to what their final days or hours are going to look like. Where are they going to be? Do they want privacy? Do they want to be alone?

Do they want shades drawn and light music? Do they want to meditate in their own space? Do they want to pray? Or do they want to be in the middle of the living room with the stereo on and the lights blaring and normal conversation going on? Again, these are the kinds of things that you have the right to set up for yourself. And you can change your mind. You may think that you want a live band playing music with yourself as the center of attention, and then find as time gets closer that you don't want that. Make sure the people around you know when you've changed your mind and that you possibly could change it again. There's no way to really understand or know how you're going to feel over time.

Michael: We've seen it all over the map. For example, being the center of attention in the middle of the living room in a hospital bed with people around you can be a wonderful setting. If you don't want certain smells, if flowers offend you, have them removed. If you like smells, have flowers or incense around. It's your moment! It's your time, and it's the only time that you have left!

Gail: Who do you want to attend your farewell party? Who in your fantasy of fantasies is there, and what are they doing? Can you ask them to be present? Or do you need to ask them to stay away?

Michael: Like John when he staged his own memorial party prior to dying. That was classic!

Gail: John wanted to attend his own memorial. He felt, "Dammit, if I'm going to die, I'm going to attend my own soiree!" And that's exactly what he did. He and his life partner put together an invitation that specifically addressed his dying. They asked people to come and say things to him while he was still alive that normally would only be said at the time of the funeral. He wanted to hear it. And there were certain things that he wanted to say back to people. So, he created this incredible forum. The caterers were brought in and the food was exactly what he would have liked had he been able to eat. He had people dress to the nth degree. This was not a sloppy, casual affair; it was almost black tie. He hired a piano player and singers. Flowers were everywhere. There were balloons outside. There was valet parking, and the entire thing was videoed. He had on a tailor-made suit and held a gold handle cane, sat himself up in a comfortable chair in the backyard beside the pool filled with floating flowers. People talked to him, and he talked back. It was probably one of the most wonderful experiences I have ever had. I also recognize that clearly there is no way that some people could do what John did. So that's an option -- if you have the energy and the personality. After John died, we had a regular funeral. We had a funeral for us, and we did it the way we needed to do it. About 20 years later, a poignant movie came out based on a similar concept and with a powerful conclusion.

The Body

Michael: What happens to "the body"? Who makes the decision? Who gets the remains? Say, for example, you are not married and you want your significant other to have your remains, but your family has reasserted themselves. How are you going to assure that your friend or life partner will get your remains? Is it important to them that you be on their mantelpiece? Or that you be buried in their city versus where you were born and raised? What do you want your documents to say? Remember those?

Gail: That's very personal, but I think in all fairness that you should really look at the "Why?" What are your motives? Why do you want control over that after you've died? Do you have a hidden agenda - perhaps getting even with someone by withholding your remains? Is it the final to "Hell with you!" to your family? Think about it.

Michael: And it may not be that you want to have control after death. It may be just one of those things that really matters to you. After you've died, where would you like to be? Would you like to be on the West Coast? The East Coast? Do you want to be scattered at sea?

Gail: That goes back to the need for closure and clear communication so that no one's feelings are hurt. If you've made up your mind that you want your ashes scattered on the West Coast, and your mother or your grandmother or your father has other wishes, then I think in all fairness you should sit down with that individual. Explain very clearly what you want and why you want it. That it's not to get even for some bad feelings from the past. Hopefully, they will feel good about it -- as clean and as healthy about that decision as about many other decisions you've made. Maybe you're an older adult with children, and maybe you're going against their fantasy. In all fairness to them, talk about it. Perhaps you can compromise with them, especially if they have strong feelings. If you have grown up with a strict cultural or religious background and that background forbids cremation, for instance, maybe you will compromise and say, "Alright, I won't be cremated, but my remains are to be in California. "There are things we can do to try to appease everyone, and I think it's important that we remember the living. Who are we leaving behind? And what kind of condition are we going to be leaving them in?

Michael: Right. Are we leaving this Planet a better place, or is it glad that we're exiting?

Gail: And don't forget along the way to have a couple of good cries with the people you love. You all deserve it!

Epilogue : The End

Michael: Our hope is that we've answered some questions for you and generated even more questions than were answered.

Gail: If you were brave enough to read this book in its entirety, then we have probably helped you with "practicing." Just by reading this, you have practiced, and hopefully you will have the courage to act on the information that we've provided.

Michael: We hope that you see the importance of open, honest, on-going communication. You need to be telling others about what's going on. You need to be communicating with your physician. You need to have a therapist or a support group or some space where you can dump --unload -- some of the stuff that's going on in your head. Also, it's important to make certain that the people in your life are the ones that you want in your life. Because they're going to be the ones you depend on to carry out your wishes. They're going to be your last fellow travelers on this trip.

Gail: Along those lines, there are a couple of other very important thoughts I'd like to repeat and leave fresh in your mind. I think one of the worst things that you can do to yourself is to ask someone who is 2,000 miles away to be on your "Durable Power of Attorney." I know that the one thing we've learned is that either you go to where they are, or you choose someone that's in the neighborhood where you wish to die. If that is where you've lived your whole life and it's important to you to remain there -- wherever "there" is -- then choose someone close, someone of like mind, not someone who has to disrupt their life and try to live for months in your home. You might not want to choose a brother or a sister who has been out of your life for twenty years: they're going to bring along all the old baggage from when you were kids -- and you've changed. But their anger, disappointments, and fantasies may not have changed.

Michael: Another important thing is making certain that you write everything down, keep a journal, take notes, make certain that your wants and wishes are in your handwriting to ensure that you've done your part, which is to pass on these messages. To pass on the information. You'll do a great disservice to the people you leave behind if you don't, and you'll leave them an incredible gift if you do.

Gail: Most importantly, we hope we've helped you understand the critical value of taking an active role in controlling your life. For this is about all of us, ill or not in this moment, living the remainder of our lives to their fullest. I see it's getting late. Shall we close for now?

Michael: Yes, I think we should bring things to a close for now. Goodnight, Gail.

Gail: Goodnight, Michael.

Photo by Lindburgh McPherson

Gail Cason-Reiser, (center) Death Doula, has been a strong, outspoken, patient advocate since contacting a life-threatening illness and beginning her own battle over 40 years ago. In addition, she was the devoted caregiver to her husband during his battle with cancer. She has led support groups and given individual counseling to those living with life-threatening and terminal illness and to their significant others, families, and friends. A frequent speaker on death and dying issues, she gives lectures to the public and caregiving professionals, provides in-service training, and often is requested to eulogize at memorials and funerals. A former business executive, she is now devoted to providing a voice for, and in support of, patients.

Michael J. Demoratz, (right) PhD, MSW, LCSW, CCM, has over 35 years' experience in hospice and palliative care. Nationally, as a recognized expert (Case Manager of the Year Award, CMSA), he has presented at hundreds of conferences and published numerous articles on end-of-life, bereavement, pain management, and catastrophic case management. He is a Board Member of the Commission for Case Manager Certification and was a 6-year former Board Member of the Coalition for Compassionate Care of California. Currently, he provides consultant services to the Memorial Healthcare System for patients and families seeking hospice and palliative care support. He has provided support for over 10,000 patients and families.

Richard J. Reiser, (left) MA, LMFT, Certified Hakomi Therapist, is a licensed family psychotherapist who has devoted himself to volunteering with the homeless, the chemically dependent, and the significant others, spouses, family, and friends of those facing life-threatening and terminal illness. A retired marketing executive and former advertising agency owner (Lifetime Achievement Award), he has experienced his own battle with cancer and his wife's 40-year struggle with her illness.

Made in the USA
San Bernardino, CA
13 November 2018